SARS-CoV-2
Contagion, Collusion, Corruption

Greg Felton

ISBN: 978-1948323-12-3

Turning the Tide Publishing
6456 Bullet Drive • Crestview • Florida • 32536
(850) 677-0344
turningthetidepublishing.com

Printed in the United States of America

QTY	SKU	ITEM
1	SARS	SARS-CoV-2

SARS-CoV-2

Contagion, Collusion, Corruption

By Greg Felton

Other works by Greg Felton

Book
The Host & The Parasite: How Israel's Fifth Column Consumed America

Anthology
Exploding Middle East Myths: 15 Years of Fighting Zionist Propaganda

Table of Contents

CONTAGION, COLLUSION, CORRUPTION

Introduction

GREAT ACTS OF VIOLENCE ARE THE FORCES THAT shape history. This is true even for democracies, which do not always live up to their humanitarian, égalitarian image. Great violence causes trauma, fear, panic and dislocation that destroy societies, and on its ruins a new social order arises but one shaped by different people and different interests.

For example, Europe was so psychologically crippled by the carnage of the First World War that any will to understand war and its causes was abandoned in favour of one that tried to moralize it out of existence. As internationalism replaced nationalism, irrationality replaced reason, and pacifism replaced realpolitik, Western democracies and governments merely reacted to the effects of war, not its cause, and in so doing ended up creating the very conditions that would make a return to war inevitable.

For the mass public, great violence cannot be objectively explained or rationally comprehended while it is occurring because it has no context: the public can only react to what it is shown, just as a movie audience sees only what the director wants the camera to reveal. Those who set the violence in motion are invisible, and do not fear reprisals. Certainly, this was true of the 2001 World Trade Center (WTC)/Pentagon attack.

On Sept. 11, and for a long time afterward, the shock of the brazen, daylight destruction of the Twin Towers and loss of life left Americans desperate for any explanation that could make sense of the horror they were witnessing . . . or thought they were witnessing. Within minutes of the first plane's "hitting" the North Tower, as if on cue, "experts" popped up on CNN's live feed to declare that "Muslim extremists" had hijacked passenger jets and flown them into the buildings despite the fact that no such information existed — still doesn't. These "instant experts" had to have known the attack was going to happen because they were available to be interviewed and obviously had been coached on what to say. What appeared to be a spontaneous act of conspicuous violence was really a stage-managed horror show.

The official story was transparently incompetent, but amid the chaos and shock few were equipped to wonder or care why there was no airplane wreckage, no human remains, and no explanation for how jet fuel could vaporize reinforced concrete buildings. The official narrative worked, though, not because it was true, but because it was simplistic, convenient and ruthlessly propagandized: it gave Americans an external enemy on which to focus their anger and bloodlust, thereby deflecting attention from the real perpetrators: the George W. Bush governing junta and Israel.[1] The lie of the Muslim hijackers spread like a virus, mutating the political culture of the U.S. and infecting the minds of billions of people worldwide.

The virus metaphor is deliberate because the WTC/Pentagon attack can help explain the SARS-CoV-2 pandemic and the way it is marketed. Each is an act of great violence caused by an unseen contagion—the former, political; the latter, biological—and propped up by a transparently contrived cover story. Dishonesty and ineptitude notwithstanding, this story becomes "the official version," while intelligent alternative theories are actively censored and their proponents ridiculed.

This book will argue that the "official" story of SARS-CoV-2's being a naturally occurring virus is scientifically unsound if not overtly dishonest; that is, this book refutes the claim that the virus jumped species directly from bat to human or through an intermediary animal. Not only is there no defensible evidence for such a claim, but the arrogant, defensive behaviour of its apologists toward any alternative explanation shows that the "official" version cannot be defended rationally and is based on political obfuscation, not scientific evidence. As one senior Trump administration official told *The Washington Post*:

> "The idea that it was just a totally natural occurrence is circumstantial. The evidence it leaked from the lab is circumstantial. Right now, the ledger on the side of it leaking from the lab is packed with bullet points, and there's almost nothing on the other side."[2]

To demonstrate that SARS-CoV-2 is not an evolutionary virus but rather a virus made from the genetic material of more than one virus and that it escaped from the Wuhan Institute of Virology, it is necessary to deal with all aspects of the natural-origin claim.

Introduction

Chapter 1 refutes the natural-origin claim on its merits, such as they are, and focuses on the belligerent conduct of its defenders. Although there is some technical nomenclature, it applies only to proper names of viruses.

Chapter 2 rebuts the scientific claim that SARS-CoV-2 evolved from SARS-Co-V. Because the evidence comes from epidemiological and genetic comparisons of the two viruses, much of the language is scientific. Important technical terms are explained, and to the largest extent possible jargon has been rendered into plain English. Of necessity this analysis is simplified, so those who want the hard, detailed science should consult the sources in the notes at the end of the book.

Chapter 3 presents evidence for synthetic origin and the attempts of the establishment media and scientific community to censor it.

Chapter 4 explains how the pandemic started and how the U.S. is arguably more responsible than China for the outbreak.

Chapter 5 examines the motive for creating pathogenic viruses and whether SARS-CoV-2 viruses should be considered a bioweapon.

Chapter 6 shows he rise of resistance to the official narrative and the possible dangers posed by a head-long rush to come up with a COVID-19 virus without going through proper testing procedures.

Port Coquitlam, B.C.
November 2020

Chapter 1
Genetic Fallacy

ON DEC. 31, 2019, THE WORLD HEALTH Organization (WHO) learned that dozens of people in Wuhan had developed pneumonia of an unknown type. Chinese doctors determined it to be a new kind of coronavirus ("novel coronavirus"). As soon as the WHO report[1] came out, Chinese authorities asserted that this new variant, like many coronaviruses, originated in bats and identified the Huanan Seafood Wholesale Market in Wuhan as the source. The market is known as a "wet" market because it sells perishable food like fresh meat, fish and produce. In short, the virus jumped (was "zoonotically transferred") directly to humans. According to Dr. Ralph Baric at the Gillings School of Global Public Health at the University of North Carolina:

> Studies have predicted the existence of nearly 5,000 coronaviruses in bat populations and some of these have the potential to emerge as human pathogens, so this is not a situation of if there will be an outbreak of one of these coronaviruses but rather when and how prepared we'll be to address it.[2]

Although this quotation comes from 2015, it states the essence of the natural, bat-man explanation: contagion by association. However, what Baric said has no specific relevance to the Huanan Market or to the new virus now called SARS-CoV-2. For one thing, the market did not sell bats[3]; for another, the first official person to be infected fell ill on Dec. 1 and had no connection to the market. Given that COVID-19, the respiratory disease caused by SARS-CoV-2, has a two-week incubation period, this person had to have been infected around mid-November, long before any public announcement about the market was made. Furthermore, a *Lancet* study found no link between the first patient and subsequent patients. Of the first 41 patients, about one third had no connection to the market. Daniel Lucey, an infectious disease specialist at Georgetown University, told *Science* magazine that this anomaly cannot not be ignored:

> "That's a big number, 13, with no [market] link. The virus came *into* that marketplace before it came out of that marketplace. China must have realized the epidemic did not originate in that Wuhan Huanan seafood market" (italics added).[4]

Indeed, the Chinese government must have known, but it needed a cover story to deflect blame from those responsible for the outbreak, but this one was hastily concocted and transparently false.

By late January 2020, nobody took it seriously, leaving the batman cover story discredited, but it could not remain discredited. If the new disease did not have a natural origin, then it had to have an unnatural one. In other words, if nature didn't do it, man did, and if man did it, the virus had to have come from a laboratory. That is something the Chinese government could not admit.

The collapse of the Huanan Market theory should have killed the natural origin theory, but because it was concocted out of political necessity, not based on scientific evidence, it could not be allowed to die. It got a sudden injection of plausibility, courtesy of a prestigious science journal and ethically flexible scientists.

Batshit Crazy

On Feb. 3, 2020, within a week of the *Science* paper's debunking the market theory, *Nature* published a paper entitled "Pneumonia outbreak associated with a new coronavirus of probable bat origin," coauthored by no fewer than 29 Chinese scientists, led by the famous, or infamous, Dr. Shi Zhengli.[5] Shi (pronounced "Shirr") is China's foremost expert on bat coronaviruses and has earned the nickname "batwoman" for her years of leading research teams into caves and mineshafts in Yunnan province to trap horseshoe bats so that the coronaviruses they carry could be isolated and identified. Shi is the director of the Center for Emerging Infectious Diseases at the Wuhan Institute of Virology (WIV), where she is building a database of animal coronaviruses that could be zoonotically transferred to humans.

The *Nature* article is significant because in it the authors claimed to have found the epidemiological progenitor of the SARS-CoV-2 virus, then called 2019-nCoV:

> Since the outbreak of severe acute respiratory syndrome (SARS) 18 years ago, a large number of SARS-related coronaviruses (Carrico's) have been discovered in their natural reservoir host, bats. Previous studies have shown that some bat SARSr-CoVs have the potential to infect humans. Here we

report the identification and characterization of a new coronavirus (2019n-CoV), which caused an epidemic of acute respiratory syndrome in humans in Wuhan, China. The epidemic, which started on 12 December 2019, had caused 2,794 laboratory-confirmed infections including 80 deaths by 26 January 2020 . . . Full-length genome sequences were obtained from five patients at an early stage of the outbreak. The sequences are almost identical and share 79.6% sequence identity to SARS-CoV. Furthermore, we show that 2019nCoV is 96% identical at the whole-genome level to a bat coronavirus.[6]

This bat coronavirus was found in the faeces of a horseshoe bat (*Rhinolophus affinis*) found in an abandoned mineshaft during a 2013 research expedition to Yunnan. The authors said this virus, which they called RaTG13, showed "high sequence identity" to 2019nCoV, and from this identity drew the following conclusion:

Using the aligned genome sequences of 2019nCoV, RaTG13 SARS-CoV and previously reported bat SARSr-CoVs, no evidence for recombination events was detected in the genome of 2019nCoV . . . RaTG13 is the closest relative of 2019nCoV, and they form a distinct lineage from other SARSr-CoVs . . . The close phylogenetic [common ancestor] relationship to RaTG13 provides evidence that 2019nCoV may have originated in bats.[7]

The discovery of RaTG13 did for SARS-CoV-2 what "Muslim hijackers" did for the WTC/Pentagon attack: it gave the public a phony external enemy and made the pandemic "make sense." When a noted Chinese virologist provides ostensible scientific evidence of bat-man transmission, when that claim is given official sanction by a prestigious journal, and when the *Nature* paper is dutifully parroted in journals and the mainstream media, who was going to argue? Who would want to?

However, the *Nature* paper cannot be accepted. Leaving aside the authors' misstating the beginning of the epidemic—Dec. 1, not Dec. 12—the claims and conclusions by the authors point to scientific malpractice.

First, the paper states that RaTG13 came from a 2013 sample, yet the world only heard about RaTG13 in the 2020 *Nature* paper. On May 30, *Spectator Australia* reported that if Shi had determined that the 2013 SARS virus and the 2019 SARS-CoV-2 virus were 96.2% identical, she had a professional duty to publish her findings about RaTG13. [8] Shu Kang, a Chinese researcher using a pseudonym to protect himself from Chinese authorities, said the code would be easy to fake:

> It takes a person less than a day to type . . . a string of letters alternating between A, T, G, and C . . . (less than 30,000 letters) in a Word file. And it would be a thousand times easier if you already have a template that is about 96% identical to the one you are trying to create. Once the typing is finished, one can upload the sequence onto the public database. Contrary to general conception, such database does not really have a way to validate the authenticity or correctness of the uploaded sequence. It relies completely upon the scientists themselves – upon their honesty and consciences. Once uploaded and released, such sequence data becomes public and can be used legitimately in scientific analysis and publications. [9]

There is no credible scientific explanation for the seven-year delay before mentioning RaTG13, especially when the sample was so close by. According to a widely cited *Wall Street Journal* article by British science journalist and author Matt Ridley, "The sample was collected by hazmat-clad scientists from the Institute of Virology in Wuhan that year [2013], stored away and forgotten until January this year . . ."[10]

In fact, the 2013 sample found in the Yunnan mineshaft did not yield the genome sequence for RaTG13 as Shi claimed; it was the genomic sequence for BtCoV/4991, which she and 13 other scientists described in a *2016* research article in *Virologica Sinica.* [11] Somehow they neglected to mention BtCoV/4991 in the 2020 *Nature* article. One coronavirus sample disappeared from the publishing record while one with identical properties was artificially back-dated and appeared out of thin air. In a May 20 preprint paper on RaTG13, two Indian scientists, Monali C. Rahalkar and Rahul A. Bahulikar, drew the appropriate conclusion:

> The genome of RaTG13 . . . shows that it is 100% similar to that of bat coronavirus BtCoV/4991, also described by Dr. Zhengli Shi and her group in 2016. BtCoV/4991 was described to be a SARS-like (SL) coronavirus from bat feces sampled in an abandoned mine from Mojiang. These facts increase the possibility that RaTG13 could be the same as BtCoV/4991.[12]

A comparison of similar passages coauthored by Shi *et al.* from the 2016 *Virologica Sinica* paper and the 2020 *Nature* paper confirmed this:

> 2016: "RaBtCoV/4991 showed more divergence from human SARS-CoV than other bat SL-CoVs and *could be considered as a new strain of this virus lineage.*"[13]

2020: "RaTG13 is the closest relative of 2019nCoV, and they form *a distinct lineage from other SARSr-CoVs . . .*" (italics added in both).[14]

At the end of July 2020, Shi formally conceded the equivalence in an email interview with *Science*, but the effect damaged her credibility even further and made a mockery of the zoonotic theory she purports to uphold. According to the interview:

> Shi explained that 4991 and RaTG13 are one and the same. The original name, she says, was for the bat itself, but her team switched to RaTG13 when they sequenced the entire virus. TG stands for Tongguan, the town in Yunnan province where they trapped that bat, she said, and 13 for the year 2013.[15]

No such detail was forthcoming in April when she was asked to explain how RaTG13 was discovered. Shi could only then state vaguely that it came from a "previously detected" genetic segment of a 2013 Yunnan Horseshoe bat (*Rhinolophus affinis*) sample, and that it happened to be 96.2% identical to the genome of SARS-CoV-2.[16]

Furthermore, the claim that BtCoV/4991 represents a bat, not a genome, contradicts the 2016 paper in which Shi and the other authors clearly identified it as a newly discovered *virus*: "Only two sequences detected in this study were homologous [similar] to betacoronaviruses. One of them [was] RaBtCoV/4991."[17]

Shi's associate Peter Daszak, president of the New York City non-profit EcoHealth Alliance and long-time financial collaborator with WIV, has yet a different story. He told the *Sunday Times* earlier in July 2020 that the name change was nothing more than updated nomenclature:

The conspiracy folks are saying there's something suspicious about the change in name, but the world has changed in six years—the coding system has changed.[18]

This makes no sense whatsoever because the last two numbers of RaTG13 refer specifically to the year of discovery and that is not a matter of nomenclature that can be changed. Moreover, this claim cannot be reconciled with what Daszak told *New York Times Magazine* just three months earlier about RaTG13's being part of a unique genome:

We found the closest relative to the current SARS-CoV-2 in a bat in China in 2013. We sequenced a bit of the genome, and then it went in the freezer; because it didn't look like SARS we thought it was at a lower risk of emerging.[19]

However, according to Alina Chan, a postdoctoral scientist at the Broad Institute of Massachusetts Institute of Technology (MIT) and Harvard, even that story may not be accurate:

I think Daszak was misinformed because the . . . data on NCBI [National Center for Biotechnology Information] clearly shows that the WIV accessed the sample repeatedly in 2017 and 2018.[20]

The timing of the announcement—early February 2020—combined with its specious scientific foundation and WIV's prior knowledge of it, makes RaTG13 appear to be a politically motivated diversion to cover up Chinese government responsibility for the pandemic and to pre-empt any serious discussion that SARS-CoV-2 was made in a lab. The best description of this comes from Steven W. Mosher:

It was the equivalent of trying to wipe the fingerprints from a gun that had just been used to commit murder. The "gun" itself couldn't be destroyed, however. In fact, the murder weapon used was busy replicating itself by the billions within each and every person who came down with the China Virus . . . Dr. Shi decided to "discover" a new bat coronavirus that was very similar to the one she had created. That "discovery" would prove that coronaviruses similar to SARS-CoV-2 were found in nature, and so deflect the growing suspicion that she had engineered it in her lab.[21]

The authors of the June 5, 2020, preprint paper, "Major Concerns on the Identification of Bat Coronavirus Strain RaTG13 and Quality of Related Nature Paper," have called on *Nature* to retract the infamous article. Demands for something to be done have already started.[22] As the *Times* reported:

> In recent weeks, academics are said to have written to *Nature* asking for the WIV to write an *erratum* clarifying the sample's provenance, but the Chinese lab has maintained a stony silence. A spokesman for *Nature* said: "Concerns relating to this paper have been brought to *Nature*'s attention and are being considered at the moment. We cannot comment further at this time."[23]

By Nov. 28, 2020, this paper had been accessed 1.03 million times and cited 3,632 times.

Publishing and propaganda

In an ironic parallel, *Nature* became the host body for an "intellectual virus" that infected the world-wide scientific community, thereby preventing rational discussion of the origin of SARS-CoV-2 to the detriment of human health. The effect of this contagion is seen in a March 7, 2020, letter signed by 27 scientists and published in *The Lancet*:

> We stand together to strongly condemn conspiracy theories suggesting that COVID-19 does not have a natural origin. Scientists from multiple countries have published and analysed genomes of the causative agent, severe acute respiratory syndrome coronavirus 2 (SARS-CoV-2), and they overwhelmingly conclude that this coronavirus originated in wildlife . . . Conspiracy theories do nothing but create fear, rumours, and prejudice that jeopardise our global collaboration in the fight against this virus.[24]

The attentive reader will notice a curious feature of this letter purporting to be scientific defence of the zoonotic origin. It consists solely of generic appeals to authority and overstated claims of consensus. On the other side, the attack on the lab-origin theory consists of an *ad hominem* deflection and emotional frothing. Symptoms of the *Nature* infection are evident in the footnoted sources, which include the authors of the original *Nature* paper, and a paper led by Kristian Andersen, an oft-cited zoonotic defender.[25]

In fact, this anomalous style of writing is easily explained. The letter is a fraud. The 27 scientists did not write it. As a result of a Freedom of Information Act (FOIA) request by the organization U.S. Right to Know (USRTK), it has been revealed that the letter was drafted by Daszak as a piece of zoonotic propaganda. It was creeated through a series of back-and-forth emails among various EcoHealth officers, including science and policy advisor Hume Field, and university researchers including Ralph Baric at UNC Chapel Hill.[26]

In one early email time-stamped Feb. 6, 2020, 12:43.40 a.m. EST, Daszak expressed his dismay that scientists "with whom [EcoHealth has] collaborated for many years" were having to defend their zoonotic views against those who argue for a lab origin. To address this grave injustice, he decided to write a "letter of support." However, the source and purpose of the letter had to remain hidden:

> Please note that this statement will not have EcoHealth Alliance logo on it and will not be identifiable as coming from any one organization or person, the idea is to have this as a community supporting our colleagues . . . This letter is carefully worded to avoid political statements, and we have been told would go a long way to supporting continued collaboration in this outbreak. [27]

The letter was also carefully worded to avoid any hint of scientific understanding. Ohio State University microbial scientist Linda Saif suggested the inclusion of a couple of statements explaining why the virus is not lab-generated, but Daszak's response was, "we should probably stick to a broad statement," [28] probably knowing full well that he had no such evidence. Despite the letter's unprofessional tone and absence of scientific merit, it was approved for publication and the *Nature* virus proceeded to mutate.

Cozy scientist/publishing relationship

In a lengthy Twitter thread on Oct. 25, 2020— *threadreaderapp.com/thread/1320344055230963712.html—*

Chan presented a series of timelines that show falsification of data, missing data and mutual referencing to such a degree that no claim of accurate, individual research on the so-called natural origin of SARS-CoV-2 can be sustained.[29]

The data are collated and displayed in a series 22 cumulative timelines, each adding information to the previous one. Of these, the following three are sufficient to show the incestuous relationship among scientific journals and the lack of professional oversight that allowed inaccurate or incomplete data about the zoonotic theory to be passed off as scientific fact.

Figure 1a: Conspicuous publication

Timeline of SARS-CoV-2-related virus data published in late 2019-2020

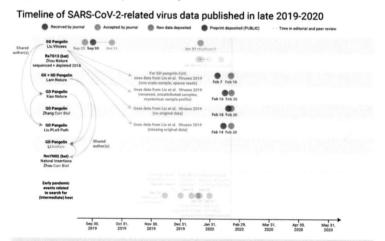

Notably, all 4 manuscripts relied heavily or solely on the 2019 data from Liu et al. **Viruses.**
Xiao et al. **Nature** renamed samples, failed to attribute these to the original study, and produced a sample profile that did not match any of the samples described in their paper.
Liu et al. PLoS Pathogens claimed to analyze a new sample but still has not shared this data.

Source: twitter.com/Ayjchan/status/1320346031427670017

The manuscripts Chan describes in Figure 1a (purple and orange circles) were all received and published by the journals *Nature, Current Biology* and *PLOS Pathogens* between Feb. 7 and Feb. 20.[30] In these, the authors claim that pangolins, scaly anteaters from Malaya, have a receptor binding domain close to that of SARS-CoV-2 and are therefore the natural mediator between bats and humans. The green arrows and type show, Chan says, that all of these journals based their claims "heavily or solely" on one source: an article led by Dr. Ping Liu that was published in October 2019. Moreover, the pangolin data in all articles also came mostly from one source.[31]

Figure 1b: Publication without evidence

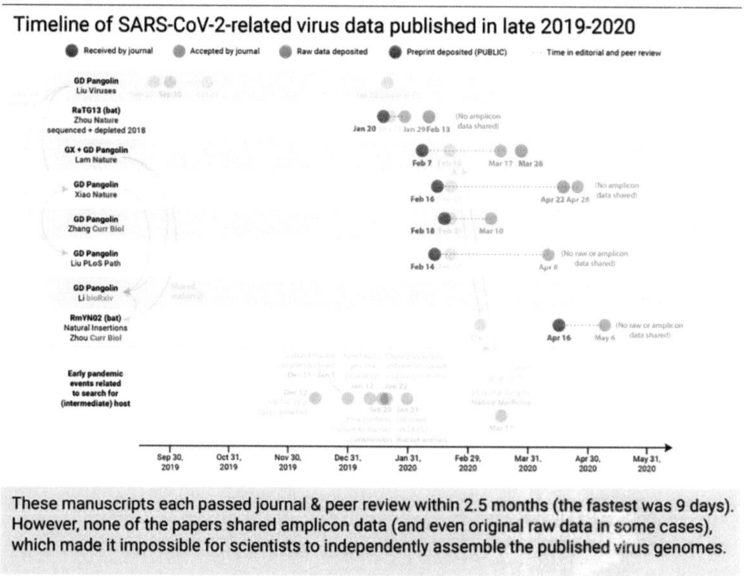

Timeline of SARS-CoV-2-related virus data published in late 2019-2020

These manuscripts each passed journal & peer review within 2.5 months (the fastest was 9 days). However, none of the papers shared amplicon data (and even original raw data in some cases), which made it impossible for scientists to independently assemble the published virus genomes.

Source: threadreaderapp.com/thread/1320344055230963712.html

Even if the claims about pangolin mediation were true, Figure 1b shows that the three above-mentioned journals accepted and published the pangolin claims without having seen the supporting raw and/or amplicon data. (The latter data refers to a DNA or RNA sequence that is the cause of, or result of, gene copying or duplication.)

In addition to the lack of originality within the zoonotic scientific community, there also appears to have been deliberate manipulation or falsification of data to force a congruence between the alleged RaTG13 genome and the raw and amplicon data, as Figure 1c shows.[32]

Figure 1c: Making the genome fit the data

Timeline of SARS-CoV-2-related virus data published in late 2019-2020

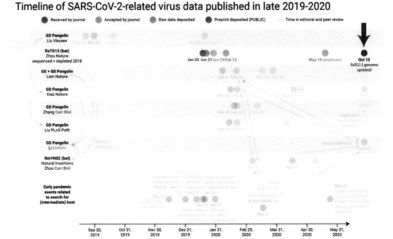

By September, scientists pointed out the mismatch between the published RaTG13 genome sequence and the raw+amplicon data. On Oct 13, the RaTG13 genome was updated on NCBI without an explanation by Zhou et al. Nature about how the original mismatch occurred and why the data was seemingly depleted for bacterial reads (what was the sample processing protocol?).

Source: twitter.com/Ayjchan/status/1320359968692895750/photo/1

In September a discrepancy between the data and the RaTG13 genome was discovered, Chan wrote, so the RaTG13 sequence of updated without any explanation from the authors of the infamous Feb. 3, 2020, *Nature* paper. The red arrow points to the surreptitious update.

Perhaps the nail in the bat-origin coffin was delivered on Sept. 18, 2020, when researchers Darja Kanduc and Yehuda Schoenfeld published a paper [33] showing "mathematically improbable" commonality of short-chain proteins (hexapeptides and heptapeptides) between SARS-CoV-2 and the human proteome.[34]

> [T]he probability of the occurrence in two proteins of just one heptapeptide is equal to $\sim 20^{-7}$ (or 1 out of 1,280,000,000). Likewise, the probability of the occurrence in two proteins of just one hexapeptide is close to zero by being equal to $\sim 20^{-6}$ (or 1 out of 64,000,000).[35]

The numbers of identical peptides are, respectively, 329 and 27, which are very close to the results for mice. (307 and 27). Significantly, there was almost no similarity with human coronaviruses.

The high degree of collusion among scientists and journals likely means that RaTG13 will not be repudiated any time soon and those responsible for SARS-CoV-2 will evade public scrutiny.

WHO is responsible?

Inasmuch as China lied about the origin of the virus, Chinese scientists fabricated data to prop up the zoonotic argument and journals gave the story legitimacy. How is it possible that WHO, which knew what was going on at WIV, did not demand an independent investigation? The answer is that it could not and would not do so.

Figure 2: Affinity of SARS-CoV-2 for human proteome

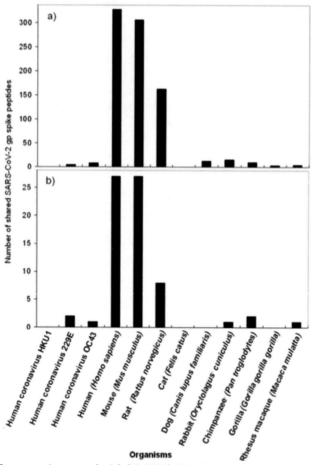

Source: springer.com/article/10.1007/s12026020091526

The number of shared peptides between the SARS-CoV-2 spike glycoprotein and mammalian and coronavirus proteomes is statistically unnatural, and the corresponding lack of affinity for bat coronaviruses virtually proves that SARS-CoV-2 did not come from nature. (TOP, hexapeptides; BOTTOM, heptapeptides)

Like any UN agency, WHO has no real independence. It must rely on funding from member states like China, and so cannot act in the public interest without risking political fallout. According to its constitution, WHO can only operate with the authority of member states, which means that its role is limited to policy and administration (normative functions); it has no *operational* function. Nevertheless, its unwillingness or inability to subject the Chinese Communist Party (CCP)'s version to critical analysis makes WHO complicit in a cover-up, and shows it to be the antithesis of the virtuous international agency it believes itself to be.

On July 31, 2020, WHO issued a report outlining the terms of reference for a future investigation into the origin of SARS-CoV-2, but right from page one, overt subservience to the CCP's zoonotic theory renders the report intellectually stillborn, as can be seen in the following excerpts:

> WHO, together with the Government of China, are setting up an international multi-disciplinary team to design, support and conduct a series of studies that will contribute to ... improving global preparedness and response to SARS-CoV-2 and zoonotic emerging diseases of similar origin.

> Current findings show that ... the virus was well adapted to human transmission from the moment it was first detected.

> Two of the genetically closest known coronaviruses, RaTG13 and RmYN02, were discovered in bat populations in Yunnan province of China (Zhou et al. 2020). RaTG13, which was identified in 2013 shares 96.2% sequence homology with SARS-CoV-2 (Zhou et al. 2020, Li W. et al 2005) while RmYN02, has 93.3 % homology.

As part of the studies conducted to help identify possible intermediary host animal(s) species for SARS-CoV-2, several susceptibility studies on a range of animal species have been performed or are underway.

It remains unclear whether the [Huanan wholesale] market was a contamination source, acted as an amplifier for human-to-human transmission, or a combination of those factors.[36]

Of course, no mention is made of investigating gain-of-function (GoF) research or a lab leak, and of course the report's sources include papers written by Kristian Andersen and the infamous *Nature* paper team.

To lay the foundation for its international zoonotic wild goose chase, WHO dispatched two animal health and epidemiology scientists on a three-week visit in July 2020, but the team's decision to bypass Wuhan intensified criticism of WHO's judgment and attitude toward the pandemic. [37] Moreover, WHO Director-General Tedros Adhanom Ghebreyesus came under criticism for his praise of China's "transparency." As Kirti Pandey, deputy news editor of India's *timesnownews* wrote:

There was mounting evidence that Chinese officials had silenced whistleblowers and undercounted cases, [yet] the WHO chief extolled praises of the leadership of Chinese President Xi Jinping. When the entire issue blew up into an escalating global health crisis — the world [was] angry that WHO's lackadaisical response potentially spurred the virus's spread.[38]

So long as WHO focuses on the spurious zoonotic theory to the exclusion of empirical evidence, any investigation into the origin of SARS-CoV-2 will be worthless, making WHO arguably a major threat to human health.

Later, in November 2020, *The New York Times* came out with a story exposing the questionable ethics underlying the investigation. WHO not only allowed China to take the lead, but the two WHO investigators refused to share their information or documents with other nations.[39] The contrast between WHO's secrecy on the one hand and its praise for China's "transparency" on the other, the *Times* wrote, is hard even for WHO's defenders to explain.[40]

For the average non-expert coping with life under the pandemic, though, the battle between scientific fact and scientific fabrication is probably not an issue; in fact, the phony RaTG13 narrative may be comforting. It explains away the pandemic as the result of an identifiable, *non-human* cause (bats), and so inhibits consideration of the disturbing, but logical, scenario of dangerously irresponsible smart people juicing the SARS-CoV virus at WIV and being collectively responsible for the deaths of more than 1.34 million people.[41]

Genetic Fallacy

Chapter 2
SARS-CoV vs. SARS-CoV-2

OVER NINE MONTHS IN 2002 AND 2003, the SARS-CoV virus caused 774 deaths in more than 24 countries. The U.S. Centers for Disease Control and Prevention (CDC) reported that international medical collaboration contained SARS-CoV within six months, and none of the eight Americans who contracted the virus died. Total cases worldwide totalled 8,096. [1]

On Feb. 8, 2020, the BBC reported that deaths from SARS-CoV-2 in Hubei province alone had already reached 780.[2] By July 21, official statistics showed that worldwide cases had ballooned to more than 15 million. At the time of writing, American deaths exceed 200,000.

Inasmuch as zoonotic defenders repeatedly chant that bats are the "natural reservoir host" for SARS coronaviruses,[3] they cannot come up with a natural, evolutionary mechanism that can explain the more than 1,828-fold increase in virulence. To prove beyond any reasonable doubt that SARS-CoV-2 and its attendant disease COVID-19 are the product of human manipulation, not natural mutation, it is necessary to take a detour into biochemistry, epidemiology and genetics. Two subtopics will be considered: how SARS viruses disrupt the body's blood-pressure regulation system and how genetic manipulation made SARS-CoV-2 unique and unnatural.

Proteins and blood pressure

At a basic level, SARS-CoV and SARS-CoV-2 are 86% genetically identical and belong to the category of βcoronaviruses, which is further divided into lineages a, b, c and d. Both belong to lineage b and both infect host cells via trimer (three-headed) spike (S) proteins. These are the many crownlike protuberances on the envelope protein surface that give the coronavirus its name.

The spike protein is divided into two domains: S1 and S2. S1 latches on to a host cell receptor, and S2 mediates virus-to-cell fusion, which permits the virus to be taken inside the host cell to commandeer its protein-making and transportation mechanisms. In both cases, it is important to understand how they use angiotensin converting enzyme 2 (ACE2) receptors as the main pathway of infection.

These receptors are found in almost all organs but especially in the heart, kidneys, intestines and most importantly in lung airways and alveolar cells in the lower lung. They are also found in the brain, testes, spleen, nasal passages, thymus, skin and bone marrow. When the S1 domain latches onto the receptors it prevents them from lowering blood pressure, which can lead to organ damage.[4]

The number and location of ACE2 receptors varies from person to person, but those with hypertension, diabetes and coronary heart disease, have more ACE2 receptors, thus making these people more susceptible to SARS viruses.[5]

The Renin-Angiotensin System

ACE2 receptors regulate the renin-angiotensin system (RAS), a hormonal cycle that regulates blood pressure. It begins when the liver secretes the long-chain protein angiotensinogen. When its first 10 amino acids are cleaved (cut) away by renin, an enzyme produced by the kidneys, it becomes angiotensin I. Angiotensin I in turn loses two more amino acids when it is cleaved by ACE (not ACE2) receptors to become angiotensin II. These receptors are secreted in the kidneys and upper lung and kidney and found throughout the circulatory system.

Angiotensin II increases blood pressure by binding to AT1 receptors to constrict blood flow and by stimulating the adrenal cortex to secrete the hormone aldosterone to tell the kidneys to retain salt, excrete potassium and retain water. To balance RAS by returning blood pressure to normal, angiotensin II binds to ACE2 receptors, which cleave it again to become angiotensin (1-7). This seven-amino acid peptide—a short protein chain of up to 100 amino acids—relaxes nitric oxide (NO), which relaxes blood vessels and reduces inflammation and hypertension. The anti-oxidizing properties of angiotensin (1-7) also protect organs from damage.

Therefore, when a SARS virus infects a cell, it not only latches onto ACE2 receptors to facilitate viral entry, but it blocks angiotensin II from being degraded to angiotensin (1-7) thereby perpetuating high blood pressure and causing severe breathing difficulty, hence the name "Sudden Acute Respiratory Syndrome."

Figure 3: The Renin-Angiotensin System

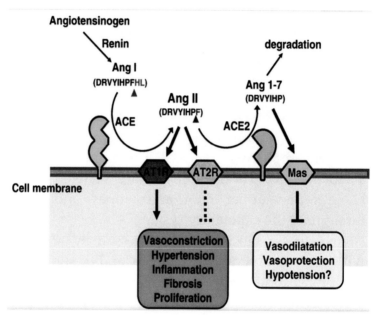

Source: semanticscholar.org/paper/TrilogyofACE2%3AApeptidaseinthesystem %2CaSARSKubaImai/c4b3097c2bf40d1c75ca5e8c2b334742cd836545/figure/1

FROM UPPER LEFT: 1) Renin cleaves Angiotensinogen into Angiotensin I, a precursor protein. 2) After losing two amino acids (red) to cleavage by ACE receptor (green), the remaining octapeptide becomes Angiotensin II, which binds to AT1 and AT2 receptors. The first receptor leads to vasoconstriction and four harmful cardiovascular effects; in contrast, AT2 receptors, found in a few organs, conversely widen and protect blood vessels. 3) Angiotensin II loses one more amino acid (purple) when cleaved by the ACE2 receptor to become Angiotensin 1-7, which binds to Mas receptors to reverse the effects of Angiotensin II by lowering blood pressure.

Cleavage basics

Another similarity is that both SARS-CoV and SARS-CoV-2 have a cleavage site on their respective spike proteins: one at the junction of the S1 and S2 domains and one on the S2 domain itself.

This latter site on both viruses performs virus–cell fusion to aid in viral replication and has a "monobasic" cleavage site; that is, the site is identified by a single amino acid from the family of basic amino acids: arginine R, lysine (K) or histidine (H). In this case, arginine.

Cleavage takes place at the surface of the host cell by the enzyme TMPRSS2 (transmembrane serine protease 2), which is found on many cell surfaces alongside ACE2 receptors in, for example, the lower lung and bronchi.[6]

It is in the S1/S2 cleavage site, however, that SARS-CoV-2 betrays signs of human manipulation. As the U.S. National Institutes of Health (NIH) reported in March 2020, the SARS-CoV-2 spike protein had an extreme binding affinity for ACE2 that is 10 to 20 times stronger than that on SARS-CoV.[7]

In other words, SARS-CoV-2 has an extreme binding affinity for human ACE2 receptors, which is contrary to nature because a virus will have a binding affinity for its "natural reservoir," bats. Nikolai Petrovsky, professor of medicine at Flinders University, said the virus's extreme affinity for *human* ACE2 receptors is so striking that he said it must either be the product of human intervention or "a remarkable coincidence."[8]

Whereas the cleavage site on the 2002–2003 SARS-CoV S1/S2 junction is also monobasic, SARS-CoV-2 has a *polybasic* cleavage site, one with more than one arginine. As the *Journal of Virology* reported in August 2008, furin cleavage sites are not found in SARS-CoV.[9] That makes

SARS-CoV-2 unique among lineage b βcoronavirus, which is why this feature is commonly called "the smoking gun" that proves man-made manipulation.

The standard model of such a site is RXXR, where R represents arginine and X can refer to any amino acid. In the case of SARS-CoV-2, the site between the S1 and S2 domains has the inserted sequence proline (P) arginine (R) arginine (R) alanine (A), which connects to an existing arginine at amino acid sequence 685. The result gives the polybasic cleavage site RRAR. The cut comes after the last arginine and is carried out by the enzyme furin, which is widely produced in many organs, particularly the lungs.

The enzyme furin is vital to human life because some proteins are dormant after being synthesized by genes and require furin to activate or "prime" them. The importance of the furin cleavage site for COVID-19 is that it not only adds a more widespread cleavage opportunity, but it enhances infectivity, as described in a June 26, 2020, paper in *iScience*:

> In addition to furin, other proteases [enzymes] also cleaved SARS-CoV-2 much more readily than SARS-CoV . . . Our data demonstrate that the S1/S2 site of SARS-CoV-2 S is efficiently cleaved by a wide range of proteases, not only furin. The comparative data with SARS-CoV S1/S2 site reveals that the acquisition of the four amino acid insert distinctively broadens the activating protease repertoire of the SARS-CoV-2 S1/S2 cleavage site to all major classes of proteolytic enzymes known to potentially activate coronavirus S proteins.[10]

Where did this polybasic site come from? Furin cleavage sites are found in other viruses like influenza, H5N1 avian flu, HIV, MERS, yellow fever, and Ebola, as shown in Table I. Note that MERS is a lineage c βcoronavirus, which is not related to SARS CoVs. This fact invites the logical hypothesis that the SARS-CoV-2 furin cleavage site was spliced into the SARS-CoV genome, specifically between amino acid sequences ("residues") 681 and 685. If true, that would make SARS-CoV-2 a chimeric (composite) virus, not a single one. This is indeed likely since this kind of splicing had been going on since at least 2006:

> To determine whether proteolytic cleavage [breaking down] of the [spike protein] might be important for the newly emerged SARS-CoV, we introduced a furin recognition site at single basic residues within the putative S1–S2 junctional region. We show that furin cleavage . . . generates discrete S1 and S2 subunits and potentiates membrane fusion activity.[11]

In plain English, this means that a polybasic site was inserted into SARS-CoV, and the result showed successful furin cleavage at the spike protein's S1/S2 junction. In fact, the site chosen in 2006 is in the same location as the PRRA insert for SARS-CoV-2.[12]

In all, 380 amino acid substitutions separate SARS-CoV-2 from SARS-CoV, something that evolution cannot adequately account for. As the authors of a March 11, 2020, article in *Cell Host & Microbe* wrote:

> Due to very limited knowledge of this novel virus, we are unable to give reasonable explanations for

the significant number of amino acid substitutions between [it] and SARS or SARS-like CoVs.[13]

Table I: Coronavirus and non-coronavirus cleavage

Polybasic cleavage sites in β coronaviruses		Polybasic cleavage sites in non-coronaviruses	
Name	Polybasic S1/S2 cleavage site	Name	Polybasic S1/S2 cleavage site
*HCoVOC43 lineage a	GYCVCYSKNRRSRGAI	HIV	VQREKRAV
HCoVHKU1 lineage b	YNSPSSSSSRRKRRSI	Influenza Virus H5	RKRKKRGL
SARS–CoV lineage b	GICASYHTVSLLRSTS (monobasic)	Avian H5N1	RERKRKKRGL
SARS-CoV-2 lineage b	ASYQTQTNSPRRARSVA	Yellow Fever	SRRSRRAI
MERS-CoV lineage c	ALPDTPSTLTPRSVRSVP	Ebola	GRRTRREA

Adapted from europepmc.org/article/med/32057769

*Human Coronavirus

The three basic amino acids (red) are arginine I, lysine (K) and histidine (H). The other letters in the chains refer to other amino acids. The standard model for a furin polybasic cleavage site is RXXR, where X refers to any amino acid. Cleavage takes place after the last arginine. Note that SARS-CoV (shaded) has only one arginine at the S1/S2 site. Therefore, it is not plausible to consider SARS-CoV the natural progenitor of the lineage b βcoronavirus SARS-CoV-2.

Epidemiological evidence aside, why should anyone take the zoonotic narrative seriously when genetic manipulation of SARS-CoV had been successfully conducted at least 13 years before the outbreak?

Table II: Nucleotide codons that encode amino acids

First Base		U		C		A		G		Third Base
				Second Base						
		U		C		A		G		
U	UUU	Phenylalanine	UCU	Serine	UAU	Tyrosine	UGU	Cysteine	U
	UUC	Phenylalanine	UCC	Serine	UAC	Tyrosine	UGC	Cysteine	C
	UUA	Leucine	UCA	Serine	UAA	Stop	UGA	Stop	A
	UUG	Leucine	UCG	Serine	UAG	Stop	UGG	Tryptophan	G
C	CUU	Leucine	CCU	Proline	CAU	Histidine	CGU	Arginine	U
	CUC	Leucine	CCC	Proline	CAC	Histidine	CGC	Arginine	C
	CUA	Leucine	CCA	Proline	CAA	Glutamine	CGA	Arginine	A
	CUG	Leucine	CCG	Proline	CAG	Glutamine	CGG	Arginine	G
A	AUU	Isoleucine	ACU	Threonine	AAU	Asparagine	AGU	Serine	U
	AUC	Isoleucine	ACC	Threonine	AAC	Asparagine	AGC	Serine	C
	AUA	Isoleucine	ACA	Threonine	AAA	Lysine	AGA	Arginine	A
	AUG	Methionine or start	ACG	Threonine	AAG	Lysine	AGG	Arginine	G
G	GUU	Valine	GCU	Alanine	GAU	Aspartic Acid	GGU	Glycine	U
	GUC	Valine	GCC	Alanine	GAC	Aspartic Acid	GGC	Glycine	C
	GUA	Valine	GCA	Alanine	GAA	Glutamic Acid	GGA	Glycine	A
	GUG	Valine	GCG	Alanine	GAG	Glutamic Acid	GGG	Glycine	G

Source: socratic.org/questions/594026e211ef6b6bf7aa8a17

Three nucleotides from among adenine (A), cytosine (C), guanine (G) and uracil (U) form an RNA codon, and one codon equals an amino acid, but more than one combination is possible. The table above contains all possible nucleotide combinations. In half of these, all four third-place nucleotides encode the same amino acid. In all, 64 codons encode amino acids, which includes three "stop codons" that nucleotide combination.

A special kind of arginine

No evolutionary explanation for the PRRA insertion can account for the rare combination of nucleotides that make up the two arginines. Four nucleotides — adenine (A), cytosine (C), guanine (G) and uracil (U) — are the building blocks of all amino acids that combine to form proteins, and each group of three nucleotides is called a codon. One codon equals one amino acid; a chain of amino acids makes a protein. In all, 64 combinations of nucleotides are possible: 61 codons (including the start codon) and three stop codons, which signal the end of protein synthesis. As Table II shows, almost all amino acids can be encoded by more than one grouping of nucleotides, for example:

Proline (P):   CCA, CCC, CCG, CCU
Serine (S):   AGC, AGU, UCA, UCC, UCG, UCU
Arginine I: AGA, AGG, CGA, CGC, CGG, CGU

Because of this redundancy, a mutation on one nucleotide will not necessarily encode a different amino acid. If the serine codon AGC mutated into AGU, it would still be a serine. On the other hand, if AGC mutated into AGA, the serine would mutate into an arginine. In the case of the arginine codons in the PRRA insert, both are CGG, and that is statistically conspicuous. As professor Rossana Sereto of the University of Innsbrück wrote:

> [T]wo CGGCGG codons . . . are quite rare for these viruses: only 5% of arginines are coded by CGG in CoV2 . . . and CGGCGG in the new insert is the *only doubled instance* of this codon in CoV2 . . . Therefore, SARS-CoV-2 remains unique among its beta coronavirus relatives not only due to a polybasic furin site at the S1/S2 junction, but also due to the four amino acid insert PRRA which had created it.[14] (italics added)

If a different nucleotide encodes the same amino acid, the mutation is called "synonymous"; if it encodes a different amino acid, the mutation is "non-synonymous." In the case of RaTG13, which zoonotics claim is nearly genetically identical to SARS-CoV-2, the syn/non-syn ratio on the S1 domain is within statistical norms, but on the S2 domain it is an utterly implausible, and unnatural, 44:1.[15] The reason for this bizarre ratio is that of the 79 nucleotide differences between RaTG13 and SARS-CoV-2 all of them except two affect the third nucleotide in each codon leading to no amino acid changes, and that is conspicuously non-random.

Table III: The 20 amino acids and their letter codes

Amino Acid	3ltr	1ltr		Amino Acid	3ltr	1ltr
alanine	ala	A		leucine	leu	L
arginine	arg	R		lysine	lys	K
asparagine	asn	N		methionine	met	M
aspartic acid	asp	D		phenylalanine	phe	F
cysteine	cys	C		proline	pro	P
glutamine	gln	Q		serine	ser	S
glutamic acid	glu	E		threonine	thr	T
glycine	gly	G		tryptophan	trp	W
histidine	his	H		tyrosine	tyr	Y
isoleucine	ile	I		valine	val	V

Another cover story

Because the PRRA furin cleavage site and its unique variety of arginine are enough to puncture the zoonotic theory, its defenders had to respond. Therefore, on May 11, 2020, the miraculous discovery of RmYN02 made its way into the scientific literature [16] one day after it appeared in the journal *Current Biology*. [17] To all appearances, the breathless announcement read like the script for the discovery of RaTG13, complete with grandiose claims of genetic similarity and incantations of the ritualistic mantra that bats are the "natural reservoir" of the SARS coronavirus.

RmYN02 ostensibly came out of a study of 227 bats from Yunnan province conducted between May and October 2019. However, the authors of this discovery, like those who gave us RaTG13, offer no empirical evidence, which suggests that RmYN02 is yet another political construct. Two features of the May 11 *Cell Press* story support this conclusion. The first is the unscientific posturing of Shi Weifeng, director of the Institute of Pathogen Biology at Shandong First Medical University and senior author of the source *Current Biology* article. The following quotation of his comes immediately after the reporter's introduction:

> Since the discovery of SARS-CoV-2 there have been a number of unfounded suggestions that the virus has a laboratory origin. In particular, it has been proposed the S1/S2 insertion is highly unusual and perhaps indicative of laboratory manipulation. Our paper shows very clearly that these events occur naturally in wildlife. This provides strong evidence against SARS-CoV-2 being a laboratory escape.[18]

Because defending the Chinese government and WIV, not scientific investigation, is Shi's prime motive, no claims he makes for RmYN02's origin can be taken at face value. The second feature is his use of it to address the PRRA furin cleavage site, the proverbial "smoking gun" that points to laboratory manipulation. Since Shi cannot deny that the site exists, he tries to coopt it by implying that SARS-CoV-2 and RmYN02 have a common origin:

> The key similarity between SARS-CoV-2 and RmYN02, is the finding that RmYN02 also contains amino acid insertions at the point where the two subunits of its spike protein meet . . . The insertions

in RmYN02 are not the same as those in SARS-CoV-2, which indicates that they occurred through independent insertion events. But a similar insertion event happening in a virus identified in bats strongly suggests that these kinds of insertions are of natural origin. "Our findings suggest that these insertion events that initially appeared to be very unusual can, in fact, occur naturally in animal betacoronaviruses," Shi says.[19]

This excerpt also contains two well-known logical fallacies. The first is "begging the question": assuming the answer that is to be proven. Even if RmYN02 acquired amino acid insertions at the S1/S2 junction through a natural "independent insertion event," it does *not* indicate that SARS-CoV-2 also did. The second is "the genetic fallacy": judging a claim to be true or false not based on its merits but solely on the claim of its origin. Shi rubbishes evidence for laboratory manipulation by denying any source for SARS-CoV-2's insertions other than nature. The claim at the end about his findings is empty.

For the record, Genbank, the NCBI genetics database, has no entry for RmYN02.

SARS-CoV vs. SARS-CoV-2

Chapter 3
Chimeric Virus

BECAUSE THE NATURAL ORIGIN THEORY HAS BEEN shown to be scientifically indefensible and rhetorically dishonest, the inevitable conclusion is that SARS-CoV-2 came from a laboratory, and that laboratory is understood to be WIV. The now obvious man-made nature of SARS-CoV-2 raises a host of unsettling questions:

- Why would such a lethal virus be created?
- How was SARS mutated to create SARS-CoV-2?
- Who was responsible?
- How did SARS-CoV-2 get out of the lab?
- Was it leaked, and if so, was it done deliberately?
- Is SARS-CoV-2 a bioweapon?

Before these questions can be addressed, though, this pandemic must not be seen as a one-off event. Tampering with viruses to make them more virulent, more transmissible to humans, is the purpose of GoF research and has been going on for decades. Perhaps the most significant aspect of the COVID-19 pandemic is that something like it had not already happened.

Carrie Wolinetz, head of the Office of Science Policy at NIH gives the standard justification for GoF research:

> "Gain-of-function experiments allow us to understand how pandemic viruses evolve, so that we can make predictions, develop countermeasures, and do disease surveillance . . . These experiments will help us get ahead of viruses that are already out there and pose a real and present danger to human health. It is the only way we can really understand at a molecular level how these processes occur, and then we can take that information to develop the tools that we need to protect against these diseases."[1]

Putting the case against GoF research is Marc Lipsitch, professor of epidemiology at Harvard and member of the Cambridge Working Group:

> I still do not believe a compelling argument has been made for why these studies are necessary from a public health point of view; all we have heard is that there are certain narrow scientific questions that you can ask only with dangerous experiments . . . There is nothing for the purposes of surveillance that we did not already know. Enhancing potential pandemic pathogens in this manner is simply not worth the risk.[2]

Milton Leitenberg, senior research associate at the Center for International and Security Studies at the University of Maryland, puts WIV's GoF research into a context that depicts the effect of COVID-19:

> The WIV began its gain of function research program for bat coronaviruses in 2015. Using a natural virus, institute researchers made "substitutions in its RNA coding to make it more transmissible. They took a piece of the original

SARS virus and inserted a snippet from a SARS-like bat coronavirus, resulting in a virus that is capable of infecting human cells." This meant it could be transmitted from experimental animal to experimental animal by aerosol transmission, which means that it could do the same for humans. In other words, *gain of function techniques were used to turn bat coronaviruses into human pathogens capable of causing a global pandemic.* (italics added)[3]

The fact that the world is now in the midst of the kind of pandemic that GoF research is supposed to prevent, reduces Wolinetz's sanguine depiction of such research to a perversity. More to the point, it demonstrates that SARS-CoV-2 could well be the result of GoF genetic manipulation. Justifying the creation of a Dr. Moreau-like hybrid of SARS-CoV with some other virus in the name of protecting people against some unknown natural outbreak is untenable since manipulating viruses in a lab to create hyper-infectious chimeric viruses is the antithesis of evolution.

Chimeric evidence and censorship

Because of the need to prop up the zoonotic narrative, no proper investigation has been conducted into the origin of the genetic material that was spliced into SARS-CoV that turned it into the chimeric SARS-CoV-2. One candidate is the lineage c βcoronavirus MERS, the only naturally occurring virus that has furin cleavage sites at both S1/S2 and S2 sites on the spike protein. [4] Furthermore, the receptor through which MERS enters host cells, transmembrane dipeptidyl peptidase 4 receptor (DDP4), can also mediate SARS-CoV-2 entry.[5] The DPP4 receptor, encoded by the gene of the same name, is found on the membrane surfaces of lungs and kidneys, much as ACE2 receptors are.

However, by far the most discussed, and contested, candidate is HIV. On Feb. 27, 2020, the *South China Morning Post* (*SCMP*) reported the results of a study conducted by a team of researchers led by professor Ruan Jishou at Nankai University that found "HIV-like" furin cleavage sites on the SARS-CoV-2 genome. The report said that the viral binding efficiency of SARS-CoV-2 is 100 to 1,000 times stronger than that of SARS-CoV and that this feature could be the result of genes not found in SARS but possibly found in HIV, Ebola or even avian flu. The findings of Ruan's team were confirmed by a research team at Huazhong University of Science and Technology in Wuhan, led by professor Li Hua.[6]

A remarkable feature of the *SCMP* article is the modest language of the scientists. None of them dogmatically asserted that HIV *was* the source of the alien gene sequence; they merely suggested that it *might* be. If so, then drugs that target the furin site could offer promise, and in that spirit Li's study cited a number of anti-HIV drugs that might have application for SARS-CoV-2: "Indinavir, Tenofovir Alafenamide, Tenofovirm Disoproxil and Dolutegravir, [as well as] hepatitis C therapeutic drugs including Boceprevir and Telaprevir."[7]

Furthermore, on June 2, a team of Norwegian and Scottish researchers — Birger Sørensen, Andres Susrud and Angus Dalgleish — published a paper in the *Quarterly Review of Biophysics*, that described, among other things, similarities in the way that SARS-CoV-2 and HIV infect host cells.

They found that the receptor binding domains (RBDs) on SARS-CoV-2, the part of the virus that latches onto the ACE2 receptor, are more alkaline (basic) and potent than those of SARS-CoV. These RBDs, like those of HIV, have loops containing segments with the amino acid cysteine (C) at either end. For example, loop 2 contains the segment NLCPFGEVFNATRFASVYAWNRKRISNCVA, where the blue Cs indicate cysteine at amino acid positions 336 and 361. The red lettering indicates the basic amino acids arginine (R) and lysine (K). In all, the scientists found four loops, one of which was not found in SARS-CoV.

The added alkalinity from numerous basic amino acids, especially lysine, greatly increases the positive charge on the loops and gives the SARS-CoV-2 RBD enhanced binding affinity for the negatively charged, acidic surface membrane on the host cell. The authors also noticed the following: "This method of action using ACE2 as main receptor . . . is similar to what is observed for HIV and its use of CD4 as main receptor."[8]

The title of the Norwegian/Scottish paper, "A Candidate Vaccine for COVID-19 (SARS-CoV-2) Developed from Analysis of its General Method of Action for Infectivity," indicates that the authors' interest in HIV is merely a means to determine the aetiology (origin) of SARS-CoV-2 so that an effective vaccine for COVID-19 can be developed:

> The logic of the design of the vaccine . . . starts with empirical analysis of the aetiology of SARS-CoV-2. Mistaken assumptions about SARS-CoV-2's aetiology risk creating ineffective or actively harmful vaccines . . . COVID-19 candidate vaccines designed without appreciating these problems may run similar risks to those experienced with HIV vaccines that failed to show protection. The possibility of inducing auto-immune responses or antibody-dependent enhancements,[9] needs to be carefully guarded against because there is published evidence that an HIV candidate vaccine has actually enhanced infectivity.[10]

Five days later, Sørensen gave an interview in which he declared the aetiology of SARS-CoV-2 to be unnatural:

> When we technically describe the virus, we see that it has not come about in a natural development. It's done by Americans and Chinese, as part of what's called "gain of function" studies. It is done all over the world. You say you don't, but it happens all the time in advanced labs.[11]

For zoonotics and their media megaphones, the HIV hypothesis has to be rubbished because no link between SARS-CoV-2 and GoF research can be admitted, regardless of the implications for human health. Therefore, informed discussion is shut down by knee-jerk attack pieces like "Don't believe the conspiracy theories you hear about coronavirus and HIV."[12]

On the same day that Sørensen gave this interview, an article on the same topic appeared in *Forbes* magazine. Not only did it attempt to discredit the idea of HIV inserts, but it openly and unapologetically misrepresented the scientists' evidence.[13]

Table IV: Sabotaging unofficial opinion

Original *Forbes* article	"Edited" *Forbes* article
"The study from Sørensen and British professor Angus Dalgleish show that the coronavirus's spike protein contains sequences that appear to be artificially inserted.	"The authors of a British-Norwegian vaccine study—accepted by the Quarterly Review of Biophysics — claim that the coronavirus's spike protein contains sequences that appear to be artificially inserted.
Sørensen told NRK that the virus has properties that differ greatly from SARS, and which have never been detected in nature. He explained that China and the United States have collaborated for many years on … "gain of function" studies…	In their paper, the Norwegian scientist Birger Sørensen and British oncologist Angus Dalgleish claim to have identified "inserted sections placed on the SARS-CoV-2 spike surface" that explains how the virus interacts with cells in the human body. Virologists, however, note that similar sections appear naturally in other viruses.
Sir [Richard] Dearlove, who was head of MI6 from 1999 to 2004, told the Daily Telegraph that the research shows that the pandemic that paralyzes the world may have started in a lab.	However, intelligence sources from Britain's MI5 dismissed the idea as "rumor and conspiracy," according to the Times of London.

Source: lewrockwell.com/2020/06/joseph-mercola/forbes-caught-in-blatant-censoring-act

The red type on the right shows how *Forbes* tried to subvert the findings of Sørensen and his colleagues. Note that *Forbes* can only cite clichéd, generic sources against the scientists' empirical data. The catchall slur "rumor and conspiracy" is evidence that the attack is driven by political, not scientific, considerations.

The article by David Nikel originally carried the heading, "Norway Scientist Claims Report Proves Coronavirus Was Lab-Made," but it was overwritten by a version that carried the heading "Controversial Coronavirus Lab Origin Claims Dismissed By Experts."

Each article carried the identical time stamp: Jun 7, 2020, 03:42pm EDT. In Table IV above, a side-by-side comparison shows how *Forbes* sabotaged its own story. The second version carried this introductory note:

> June 8: This article has been substantially updated [sic] to reflect criticism of the published study, along with the general scientific consensus on COVID-19. It also clarifies Sørensen's financial interest in the development of the Biovacc19 coronavirus vaccine. This context did not appear in the original post. June 10: Updated with additional comment from Gunnveig Grødeland.[14]

To call this hatchet job an update is indefensible: it stands Sørensen's argument on its head; it justifies rubbishing his findings based on a non-existent consensus; it bases scientific accuracy not on evidence but on collective opinion; and it introduces irrelevant personal information. *Forbes*'s misconduct is preserved in a curious hybrid Twitter post by Nikel (below), in which the original headline and supportive comment from Richard Dearlove sandwich the later, negative headline.

The preceding may be the most brazen attempt at mainstream media sabotage of evidence that SARS-CoV-2 might contain HIV or HIV-like genomic inserts, but it was not the first or even the most consequential.

David Nikel @davidnikel · Jun 7
Norway Scientist Claims Report Proves Coronavirus Was Lab-Made via
@forbes

Controversial Coronavirus Lab Origin Claims Dismissed By Experts
Norwegian scientist Birger Sørensen's claim that the coronavirus was
man-made has been backed by former MI6 chief Richard Dearlove b...
🔗 forbes.com

Source: twitter.com/davidnikel/status/1269716475918589954

The Indian paper

On Jan. 30, 2020, a team of nine Indian researchers in New Delhi published a preprint paper in which they argued that four insertions in the SARS-CoV-2 spike protein point to HIV as the likely source. These insertions contained the following amino acid sequences: GTNGTKR, HKNNKS, GDSSSG and QTNSPRRA.[15] Note particularly the last one because it contains the polybasic cleavage site unique to SARS-CoV-2. In a personal interview with the author, one of the researchers said they were the first to point it out.[16]

> We took four different sequences, and we determined they were likely to have come from HIV. One sequence from HIV could match one from another virus. Two sequences would be rare. Three sequences would be very rare. Four

sequences would not be possible because they are not found in any other genomic sequence.[17]

Figure 4: BLASTp results for insert GTNGTKR (excerpt)

```
Query #1: INSERT_1 Query ID: lcl|Query_13010 Length: 8

Sequences producing significant alignments:

Query   E   Per.

cover Value Ident  Accession
envelope glycoprotein [Human immunodeficiency virus 1]
75%   286   100.00 AFU28737.1
envelope glycoprotein [Human immunodeficiency virus 1]
75%   286   100.00 AFU28711.1
envelope glycoprotein [Human immunodeficiency virus 1]
75%   286   100.00 AFU28717.1
envelope glycoprotein [Human immunodeficiency virus 1]
75%   286   100.00 AFU28733.1
envelope glycoprotein [Human immunodeficiency virus 1]
75%   286   100.00 AFU28693.1
envelope glycoprotein [Human immunodeficiency virus 1]
75%   286   100.00 AFU28721.1
envelope glycoprotein [Human immunodeficiency virus 1]
75%   286   100.00 AFU28699.1
envelope glycoprotein [Human immunodeficiency virus 1]
75%   286   100.00 AFU28729.1
envelope glycoprotein [Human immunodeficiency virus 1]
75%   286   100.00 AFU28705.1
envelope glycoprotein [Human immunodeficiency virus 1]
```

Source: Complete BLASTp results for GTNGTKR, HKNNKS, GDSSSG and QTNSPRRA via interview with the author

BLAST (Basic Local Alignment Search Tool) compares genomic sequences; in this case, it matched proteins (BLASTp). The eight amino acid sequence from SARS-CoV-2 matched 75% of the length of an HIV segment (query cover), and all proteins within that segment aligned perfectly (100% identity). The evalue is the number of hits that could be expected by chance. An e value of 286 means up to 286 hits of this insert could be random. Accession is a unique ID number for each sequence. If nothing else, this data proves that segments of SARS-CoV-2 do match HIV inserts.

After it came out, the authors came under attack from those who mocked their findings, said their sequences were too short and accused them of claiming SARS-CoV-2 was a bioweapon. (See Chapter 5). In response to the hostility, the authors pulled their paper with the following explanation:

> We withdrew the paper because we were shocked and surprised by the reaction in the comments. We also received 450 emails from Chinese students and other Chinese asking if this paper was even real, calling our work inaccurate, or claimed we said that SARS-CoV-2 could be used for a bioweapon. We never claimed that. Then RaTG13 came out and that pushed us to think that maybe something was wrong with our data, so we took another look. We had never experienced such a reaction, so we decided to pull the paper.[18]

After the paper was pulled, the researchers conducted sequence comparisons between HIV and SARS-CoV and found no matches, whereas comparisons with SARS-CoV-2 showed HIV matching all four segments. The researchers confirmed the accuracy of their findings and tried to resubmit the paper three times. Each time it was rejected without review.

'RaTG13 virus' attacks HIV inserts

On its merits, the subject of HIV inserts is a mundane scientific matter, but scientific considerations are absent in the rabid denunciations oozing from the "legitimate" media. To respect the evidence that points to inserts from HIV (or any other virus) would entail having to admit that SARS-CoV-2 is man-made, and this cannot be permitted. The damage that would be done to political and scientific reputations and the myth of GoF benevolence is too high.

A particularly malicious attack appeared on the misnamed website *factcheck.org*. Its science "journalist" Jessica McDonald peppers her prose with judgmental labels like "highly dubious scientific paper," "false idea," "bogus analysis" and "conspiracy theory," all of which speak to unprofessionalism and the implication that the Indian paper has no facts to check.

Distortion like this is a necessary feature of *factcheck.org* because, contrary to its name, it has nothing to do with facts or checking: it is a gatekeeper for official narratives and a smearer of informed dissent. As the editor's note at the end says: "FactCheck.org is one of several organizations working with Facebook to debunk misinformation shared on social media."

As a result, the reader is fed a stew of *ad hominem* slurs and rhetorical fallacies dressed up to resemble respectable journalism. Although the subject of rhetorical fallacies has been mentioned in connection with zoonotic apologetics, this one deserves special comment. Below, excerpts (italics) are organized under the respective fallacy or fallacies.

FALSE CLAIM

As for the general notion that the virus has been bioengineered, there's no evidence that's true.

[W]hen engineering occurs, it's usually to bring about a meaningful change to the virus — but there's no evidence of that in the 2019nCoV genome.

McDonald may not like the Indian authors' evidence for HIV inserts, but she may not say the evidence does not exist. The second excerpt, paraphrasing the comment of computational biologist (not virologist) Trevor Bedford, is preposterous since, as this book has shown, changes to the genome, like the polybasic PRRAR site, are published fact.

SWEEPING GENERALIZATION + APPEAL TO AUTHORITY

Scientists with expertise in viral genomics, however, say that no such evidence exists. Kristian Andersen, the director of infectious disease genomics at the Scripps Research Translational Institute, told us in an email that in both cases, the analyses are "completely wrong."

The unmistakable inference here is that *all* "scientists with expertise in viral genomics," reject HIV inserts, but Norwegian virologist Birger Sørensen would beg to differ, so on that count alone the sweeping generalization is invalid. Kristian Andersen is a known supporter of the zoonotic claim, so the appeal to him as an authority creates a tautology. Besides, just because an "expert" says that something is true or false doesn't make it so.

SUPPRESSED EVIDENCE + CONFIRMATION BIAS

The short proteins the Indian scientists found to be similar to HIV are not from HIV at all, Andersen said, but are the result of the natural evolution of coronaviruses. "Had the authors compared nCoV to related bat viruses (and not just SARS as they did)," he wrote, "they would have realized that the peptides are also present in the bat viruses — and most certainly don't come from HIV."

Andersen ignores the Indian researchers' findings that *did* show matches to HIV ("not from HIV at all") and proceeds to make the standard boilerplate claim for evolution without mentioning the genetic anomalies that render such a claim absurd. Andersen, a believer in RaTG13, also failed to mention that Shi Zhengli and Peter Daszak admitted that RaTG13 does not exist in its own right, thus proving confirmation bias.

CONFIRMATION BIAS + SWEEPING GENERALIZATION + RED HERRING

On the contrary, as we've explained before, all lines of evidence point to the virus coming from an animal.

Again, if the virus had been engineered, one might expect many of the changes to cluster in one or two genes, but that's not the case here. All of this argues against the idea of the new virus having come out of a lab.

All lines of evidence?! The comment about genes and clustering is a deflection tactic that has nothing to do with evidence for HIV inserts, and McDonald is not qualified to make virologic judgments on her own. As for "explained before," the link takes the reader to another *factcheck.org* piece, but it has nothing to do with animal origin.

GUILT BY ASSOCIATION + AD HOMINEM + RED HERRING

"Well after the preprint was withdrawn, a website that traffics [sic] in vaccine misinformation, Health Impact News, also highlighted the invalid HIV connection.

Alex Jones, the conspiracy theorist . . . also waded into the coronavirus misinformation pool.

There is no place for such derogatory imputations in a rational argument. Why it was included can only be explained by the need to smear a dissenting opinion.

Whether or not one agrees with the link between SARS-CoV-2 and HIV, there can be no doubt that the conclusions of Sørensen et al. and the Indian researchers are rational and based on honest scientific investigation. In fact, if another group of scientists were to prove that the genomic inserts came from elsewhere—say, influenza or Ebola—there would be no objection because determining an accurate aetiology of SARS-CoV-2, not dogmatic defence of HIV, is what matters.

It is the uncompromising, hostile tone, more than the emptiness of the rhetoric, that undermines the zoonotic argument against HIV inserts and against a lab origin in general. How else to interpret this preposterous outburst from Shi Zhengli:

> U.S. President Trump's claim that SARS-CoV-2 was leaked from our institute totally contradicts the facts. It jeopardizes and affects our academic work and personal life. He owes us an apology.[19]

To take the scientific evidence for zoonotic origin seriously makes as much sense as believing that a passenger jet could collapse a reinforced-steel office tower onto its footprint.

Chimeric Virus

Chapter 4
Sources of the Contagion

AFTER DETERMINING THAT SARS-COV-2 MUST BE the result of GoF research carried out at WIV, it is not a big leap to conclude that the virus had to come from there. Nevertheless, this is also dismissed out of hand, but the denial does more to support the idea than refute it.

WIV director Wang Yanyi called the suggestion of a lab leak "pure fabrication,"[1] but nevertheless followed orders to initiate a cover-up. As PBS *NewsHour*'s foreign affairs and defense correspondent Nick Schifrin reported:

> On January 1, Wuhan Institute of Virology's director general, Yanyi Wang, messaged her colleagues, saying the National Health Commission told her the lab's COVID-19 data shall not be published on social media and shall not be disclosed to the media. And on January 3, the commission sent this document, never posted online, but saved by researchers, telling labs to destroy COVID-19 samples or send them to the depository institutions designated by the state.[2]

On Feb. 14, 2020, China's Ministry of Foreign Affairs issued a communiqué in which President Xi Jinping called for new legislation on biosecurity to be accelerated.[3] On March 25, the Chinese government seized complete control, issuing an edict requiring all university research papers on the origin of SARS-CoV-2 to be submitted to the education ministry and then be vetted by a special task force because some researchers had challenged the official narrative of initial human-to-human contact.[4] According to *The Washington Post*:

> The Shanghai lab that published the novel coronavirus genome on Jan. 11 was quickly shut down by authorities for "rectification." Several of the doctors and journalists who reported on the spread early on have disappeared.[5]

Despite these events, Thomas Gallagher, a virus expert and professor at Loyola University of Chicago, still denied the obvious:

> "Suggesting that SARS-CoV-2 is a purposely manipulated laboratory virus or a product of an accidental laboratory release would be utterly defenseless, truly unhelpful, and extremely inappropriate.[6]

The fact that Yanyi Wang's actions begin on Jan. 1, 2020, right on the heels of the WHO outbreak announcement,[7] confirms that the subsequent wet market and RaTG13 stories were hasty improvisations. The good news is that the feebleness of these scenarios militates against the claim that China released the virus deliberately in furtherance of some economic, military or political objective. The leak and its cover stories had none of the calculated, long-term subversive planning and firm narrative control that was associated with the September 2001, Israeli-led attack on the WTC/Pentagon.[8]

Plausible scenarios

There are a few different ways that such a biosafety failure could occur: a laboratory accident leading to an unintentional release of a chimeric virus, direct transmission from bat to lab worker, or direct transmission from bat to lab animal to lab worker. Still other scenarios involve improper disposal of lab animals and waste.

To take one example, in April 2004, an accidental SARS leak occurred at the Chinese Institute of Virology, part of China's Center for Disease Control and Prevention. The Beijing lab is a Biosafety Level 3 (BSL3) facility, where the SARS handling research guidelines were deemed "acceptable" by WHO. According to WHO spokesman Bob Dietz, two researchers—a 26-year-old female and a 31-year-old male—became infected in separate incidents.[9] The female, a postgraduate student, was admitted to hospital on April 4, whereas the male, a postdoctoral researcher, fell ill 17 days later. The infected female proceeded to go on a long train ride within China, but WHO Beijing said there was no cause for alarm.[10]

China's history of poor biosafety procedures makes categorical denials of the possibility of lab leakage impossible to take seriously, which of course makes the possibility of lab leakage more plausible. In fact, WIV's deputy director Yuan Zhiming last year wrote a paper admitting that safety and security are chronic problems:

"Most laboratories lack specialized biosafety managers and engineers. This makes it difficult to identify and mitigate potential safety hazards."[11] This is not a new problem, but one that goes back to the beginnings of WIV.

France frozen out

The idea began with the signing of a memorandum of understanding between China and France on Jan. 28, 2004. In October of that year, during a visit to Beijing, French Prime Minister Jacques Chirac sealed an agreement with his Chinese counterpart to work together to fight emerging infectious diseases. Giving this motive added urgency was the possibility that H5N1 avian flu could attack China.[12]

The project to build it was structured as a collaborative effort in which the lab would be modeled on France's lab in Lyon. From the outset, the French had concerns about China's motives and transparency. Former germ warfare experts feared China might use the new lab to create biological weapons, and the French collaborators were taken aback by China's refusal to explain what would become of the mobile P3 (BSL3) labs that the French government had paid for. One fear was that they would be put to the same use as the P4 (BSL4) lab, the implication being biological warfare.

Although the Wuhan lab was designed by French engineers and technicians, the Chinese took control of most of its construction, which did not sit well with the French who had concerns about the quality of construction as it pertained to safety, in particular the effectiveness of compartment seals. One French company, Technip, refused to certify the lab.

In 2015 Alain Mérieux resigned as copresident of the bilateral committee overseeing the project after seven years because he accepted that the P4 lab was "a very Chinese tool" despite the French knowhow that made it possible. In the end, the French derived no benefit from the project. Fifty researchers who were supposed to spend five years in Wuhan working the lab never left France. The result was that WIV was built with the latest French electronics and other materials but without French oversight.

Also in 2015, WIV was formally commissioned, and in that year its researchers helped create a chimeric coronavirus based on the horseshoe bat virus SHC014 to see how it could be made to infect humans.[13] Simon Wain-Hobson, a virologist at the Pasteur Institute in Paris, acknowledged at the time that the results showed that the novel virus "grows remarkably well" in human cells but criticized the study for providing little benefit or any useful information about the risk that a naturally occurring SHC014 virus would pose to humans.[14]

Despite the ultramodern WIV, China has not been able to shake the reputation of having substandard biosafety practices. Xiao Botao a professor at South China University of Technology, told Radio France in April that Tian Junhua, a virologist at the Wuhan Center for Disease Control 280 meters from the Huanan market, had more than once been splattered with bat blood or urine and had to self-quarantine for 14 days.[15]

Huang Yanzhong, a senior fellow for Global Health at the Council on Foreign Relations, said that in January 2020 a well-known scientist, Li Ning, received a prison sentence of 12 years for selling lab animals to local markets for human consumption.[16]

WIV's dubious safety reputation was acutely felt in the U.S., which took extraordinary oversight measures. As *The Washington Post* reported:

> In January 2018, the U.S. Embassy in Beijing took the unusual step of repeatedly sending U.S. science diplomats to the Wuhan Institute of Virology (WIV) [ending on March 27] . . . What the U.S. officials learned during their visits concerned them so much that they dispatched two diplomatic cables categorized as Sensitive But Unclassified back to Washington. The cables warned about safety and management weaknesses at the WIV lab and proposed more attention and help. The first cable . . . warns that the lab's work on bat coronaviruses and their potential human transmission represented a risk of a new SARS-like pandemic.[17]

Indeed, this is what has happened, but to lay *all* the blame for the current pandemic at the feet of China would be simplistic and unfair. Without U.S. funding and the collusion of various governmental and nongovernmental organizations, the pandemic would never have happened.

SARS-CoV-2's American parentage

U.S. responsibility for the pandemic can be dated to July 11, 2014, when the CDC reported details on two domestic releases of pathogens earlier that year. In June, personnel at the CDC's Roybal Campus in Atlanta, site of the BSL3 Emerging Infectious Diseases Laboratory, were exposed to "potentially viable" anthrax. The report stated that researchers, who were not wearing protective equipment, moved the pathogens to a lab with a lower biosafety level and handled it thinking it was inactive. The second event occurred earlier at the CDC's influenza laboratory when a sample of non-pathogenic avian influenza was contaminated with the highly pathogenic H5N1 strain and shipped to a U.S. Department of Agriculture BSL3 lab. [18] Even though nobody was affected in either incident, the CDC took action:

> As a result of these two incidents, CDC is issuing, effective immediately, a moratorium on the movement (i.e., transfer inside or outside the agency) of biological materials (i.e., infectious agents, active or inactivated specimens) from BSL3 or BSL4 facilities. The moratorium will remain in place pending review by an advisory committee.[19]

These events were not unique, nor should they have come as a surprise. From the 1980s to 2007, U.S. biolabs were involved in 53 incidents involving the release of toxic substances or the failure to follow safety procedures:[20]

Environmental release	4
Intentional release (see footnote 20)	1
Containment/security failure	7
Missing samples	3
Exposure/infection of personnel	35
Transportation/non-exposure of personnel	1
Maintenance failure/Oversight	1
Unauthorized study	1

As a result of the July 11, 2014, CDC press release, President Barack Obama decided that the risk of a pandemic from a lab accident was too high, so on Oct. 17, 2014, instituted a moratorium on GoF funding:

> [T]he U.S. Government will institute a pause on funding for any new studies that include certain gain-of-function experiments involving influenza, SARS, and MERS viruses. Specifically, the funding pause will apply to gain-of-function research projects that may be reasonably anticipated to confer attributes to influenza, MERS, or SARS viruses such that the virus would have enhanced pathogenicity and/or transmissibility in mammals via the respiratory route.
>
> During this pause, the U.S. Government will not fund any new projects involving these experiments and encourages those currently conducting this type of work—whether federally funded or not—to voluntarily pause their research while risks and benefits are being reassessed. The funding pause will not apply to the characterization or testing of naturally occurring influenza, MERS, and SARS viruses unless there is a reasonable expectation that these tests would increase transmissibility or pathogenicity.[21]

Even though the requirement for a *voluntary* halt to *current* GoF research took a lot of the force out of the announcement, there can be no doubt about the government's intentions. It wanted these experiments to stop. That didn't happen. In 2015, in direct violation of the spirit, if not the letter, of Obama's moratorium, Dr. Anthony Fauci, director of the National Institute of Allergy and Infectious Diseases (NIAID), outsourced GoF research to the newly operational WIV. Moreover, he licensed it to *continue* receiving U.S. government funds through Peter Daszak's EcoHealth Alliance. [22] This was all made possible because the original grant had been issued in 2014, and Daszak simply chose not to comply with the moratorium, which was driven by the overdue acknowledgment that GoF research represents a clear and present danger to human life.

Nature may hold many dangerous viruses, but artificially enhancing their pathogenicity in a lab takes nature out of the equation. In the case of SARS-CoV-2, the world wouldn't be scrambling to find a COVID-19 vaccine if scientists had not created the disease. The claim that such research is necessary for the development of vaccines *in case* of a pandemic renders any epidemiological justification tautological and absurd. A *financial* justification for GoF research, though, is more obvious.

Pathogens and profit

Since 2003, EcoHealth Alliance has received $100 million in federal grants, subgrants and contracts from federal agencies like the Department of Defense (DoD), Department of Homeland Security (DHS), Department of Health and Human Services (HHS) and the U.S. Agency for International Development. [23] In 2016, the year after WIV started up, the amount of EcoHealth's annual government grants exceeded the previous year's total income.

As far as China is concerned, part of a 2013 HHS grant was applied to GoF research on coronaviruses at WIV. The following year, NIAID approved a five-year,

$3.7 million grant to EcoHealth Alliance to study the risk of bat coronavirus emergence.[24]

Table V: EcoHealth Alliance gov't funding, 2015–18

	FY2015	FY2016	FY2017	FY2018
Gov't grants	$8,602,395 84% of total	$10,971,562 91% of total	$12,872,573 91% of total	$15,085,333 91% of total
Total Income	$10,189,339	$12,113,732	$14,204,993	$16,546,749

Source: ecohealthalliance.org/financials-strategy

Also in 2014, NIH approved a five-year grant of $3.1 million to EcoHealth, of which Daszak gave Shi $599,000 to conduct lab sequencing to identify potentially dangerous bat coronaviruses.[25] Nowhere in all of this largesse is GoF manipulation mentioned, just as it was never mentioned in connection with Shi in the infamous Feb. 3, 2020, *Nature* paper.

The NIAID and NIH grants, it should be noted, do not cover GoF research; neither does the HHS grant. HHS was prohibited from engaging in GoF research, but that changed on Dec. 19, 2017, when the Trump administration took the advice of the National Science Advisory Board for Biosecurity (NSABB) to end Obama's moratorium.

NSABB, a panel of seven experts, is drawn from various government departments including HHS, where Fauci just happens to be a member. NSABB's recommendation and Trump's acquiescence set in motion the conditions that would give the world the SARS-CoV-2 pandemic.[26]

A return to madness

The return of GoF funding came with a price, but a mild one. As a trade-off, NIH was required to establish the Potential Pandemic Pathogen Care and Oversight (P3CO) committee to ensure that any of Daszak's collaborators who might work under contract with HHS received committee approval before being allowed to conduct any GoF research.[27] Because such research concerns enhanced viruses, the committee's oversight did not extend to reviews of the sampling and sequencing of viruses that were already deemed to be "Potential Pandemic Pathogens."[28]

The committee was also highly secret. The names of its members were not published and the public had no idea what its decisions were of what GoF experiments might be approved. In short, the public was not allowed to know that their lives were put at risk.[29]

For example, in January 2018, two GoF projects to enhance the lethality of the highly infectious and lethal H5N1 virus was approved: one at the University of Wisconsin (Madison) and the other at the Erasmus University Medical Center in Rotterdam, The Netherlands. Earlier, in 2011, the respective researchers, Yoshihiro Kawaoka and Ron Fouchier, proudly declared that they had successfully mutated the virus to infect ferrets. Critics pointed out that the virus could now jump to humans, and the furor led to a voluntary moratorium on H5N1; that is, until new oversight regulations were implemented in 2013. For his part, Fauci actively promoted their work. As *Newsweek* reported:

He argued that the research was worth the risk it entailed because it enables scientists to make preparations, such as investigating possible antiviral medications, that could be useful if and when a pandemic occurred.[30]

Fear of a nationwide pandemic—H5N1 has a fatality rate of 50%—combined with chronic lab accidents, led Obama to declare the moratorium. The publicly funded January grant Kawaoka and Foucher received is identical to the one that caused the panic.[31]

Regarding GoF research on SARS and bat coronaviruses, the U.S. government renewed the original 2014 GoF grant for another five years on July 19, 2019. Total funding from Daszak via NIH amounted to $3,378,896. As project leader Daszak stated, manufacturing infection affinity is the key research objective behind the latest grant:

> We will use S protein sequence data, infectious clone technology, *in vitro* and *in vivo* infection experiments and analysis of receptor binding to test the hypothesis that % divergence thresholds in S protein sequences predict spillover [animal-to-human] potential.[32]

One could plausibly argue that Fauci, through Daszak, made the SARS-CoV-2 pandemic possible. Former New York Mayor Rudolph Giuliani said as much to radio host John Catsimatidis on April 26, 2020:

> Back in 2014, the Obama administration prohibited the U.S. from giving money to any laboratory, including in the U.S., that was fooling around with these viruses. Prohibited! Despite that, Dr. Fauci gave $3.7 million to the Wuhan laboratory—even after the State Department issued reports about how unsafe that laboratory was, and how suspicious they were in

the way they were developing a virus that could be transmitted to humans . . . Just think of it: If this laboratory turns out to be the place where the virus came from, then we paid for it. We paid for the damn virus that's killing us.[33]

Reversal of funding

The onset of the SARS-CoV-2 pandemic occasioned another funding change, this one directed specifically at EcoHealth Alliance and its funding of GoF research at WIV. On April 24, 2020, NIH Deputy Director for Extramural Research Michael Lauer sent Daszak an email in which he said the grant, renewed in 2019, was rescinded with immediate effect. After emphasizing that the grant was given at the discretion of NIH, Lauer said, "NIH does not believe that the current project outcomes align with the program goals and agency priorities."[34]

On the face of it, this was a bizarre decision because NIH is deeply in bed with EcoHealth and knew full well what was going on at WIV. When, exactly, did Lauer realize that "Understanding the Risk of Bat Coronavirus Emergence" was a project incompatible with NIH's priorities?

It turns out that Lauer was just doing as he was told. As Fauci told *politico.com,* the order to cancel the $3 million grant came directly from the White House: "It was canceled because NIH was told to cancel it. I don't know the reason, but we were told to cancel it."[35] The cancellation was made after the GoF project was linked with WIV, which the Trump administration believes to be the source of the pandemic.

The reaction to the NIH decision was predictable. An April 30 story in *Science* carried the headline, "NIH's axing of bat coronavirus grant a 'horrible precedent' and might break rules, critics say."[36]

The New York Times reported that 77 Nobel Laureates signed a letter of protest to the government calling the decision "preposterous" and that 31 scientific societies condemned NIH for "[setting] a dangerous precedent [by] revoking a grant that was awarded based upon scientific merit"[37]

Protesting the funding cut in the name of scientific research would have carried more weight if so much attention had not been paid to rubbishing the WIV origin of the pandemic on political grounds with the cognitively dissonant epithet "conspiracy theory," as did *politico.com* and other outlets of the pro-zoonotic mass media. [38]

Figure 5: April 24 email from Lauer to Daszak

April 24th email from Lauer to Daszak:

I am writing to notify you that the National Institute of Allergy and Infectious Diseases (NIAID), an Institute with the National Institutes of Health (NIH), under the Department of Health and Human Services (HHS) has elected to terminate the project *Understanding the Risk of Bat Coronavirus Emergence*, funded under grant R01 AI110964, for convenience. This grant project was issued under the authorization of Sections 201 and 405 of the Public Health Service Act as amended (42 USC 241 and 284). This grant was funded as a discretionary grant as outlined in the NIH Grants Policy Statement which states that the decision not to award a grant, or to award a grant at a particular funding level, is at the discretion of the agency, in accordance with NIH's dual review system.

At this time, NIH does not believe that the current project outcomes align with the program goals and agency priorities. NIAID has determined there are no animal and human ethical considerations, as this project is not a clinical trial, but rather an observational study.

Source: sciencemag.org/sites/default/files/Lauer.Daszak.NIH grant killed.partial email transcripts.April 2020.pdf

In this regard, the language in the *Science* headline is noteworthy and invites comparison to the 2011 H5N1 GoF furor. At the time, Kawaoka and Fouchier voluntarily agreed to a temporary moratorium even though their dangerous experiments did not cause a pandemic. By April 2020, the SARS-CoV-2 pandemic had been raging for four months, yet Daszak would not consider halting coronavirus research. According to him, EcoHealth was not funding SARS-CoV-2 research but rather searches for bat coronaviruses in rural China to determine which were a "high risk" of becoming infectious. This claim of benign intent is patently dishonest. For one thing, it contradicts Daszak's own description of the key objective of the cancelled project, which was *to manufacture infection affinity*.[39]

Second, Shi Zhengli admitted the GoF intent in a December 2018 paper:

> [L]ittle is known about the replication and pathogenesis of these bat viruses. Thus, future work should be focused on the biological properties of these viruses using virus isolation, reverse genetics and in vitro and in vivo infection assays. [40]

Third, Daszak's response contradicts Fauci, who defended the GoF feature of the WIV project.[41]

Re-reversal of funding

After the attack on the funding cut, NIH reversed itself again. On July 8, 2020, Lauer reinstated the grant but immediately suspended it pending EcoHealth's fulfillment of certain conditions. In his latest letter to EcoHealth, Lauer wrote:

The NIH has received reports that the Wuhan Institute of Virology ... has been conducting research at its facilities in China that pose serious biosafety concerns . . . and that EcoHealth Alliance hasn't satisfied its obligations to monitor [its partner.][42]

For the grant to be reinstated, Lauer said EcoHealth would have to fulfill certain conditions, which include:

• Providing a sample of the pandemic coronavirus that WIV used to determine its genetic sequence;[43]

• Arranging for an outside inspection of WIV and its records "with specific attention to addressing the question of whether WIV staff had SARS-CoV-2 in their possession prior to December 2019";

• Explaining purported restrictions at WIV, including "diminished cellphone traffic in October 2019, and the evidence that there may have been roadblocks surrounding the facility from October 1419, 2019"; and

• Providing the NIH with the lab's responses to the State Department's 2018 cables regarding safety concerns.[44]

Lauer's assessment is undoubtedly correct, but the timing and language of the letter raise certain questions: How is it possible that NIH did not know what EcoHealth had been funding since 2014? When, exactly, did NIH receive these reports of biosafety concerns? Why did it take a government edict to force NIH to do what it should have done years ago? Adding to the disingenuous appearance of Lauer's letter is that just two months earlier, NIH told *Newsweek* there was no scientific evidence that the SARS-CoV-2 virus was created in a laboratory.[45]

From Daszak's perspective, NIH's new terms seem to be an improvement over outright withdrawal since they at least give EcoHealth the chance to earn the grant back. Yet the nature of the conditions, reasonable though they may seem, are disquieting because satisfying them would expose the scientific chicanery behind the zoonotic theory. Of these four conditions, the first two are the most significant. The sample requested is for RaTG13, which never existed, and the second refers to the reason for the seven-year storage of BtCoV/4991, which turned out to be the real RaTG13.

The third condition addresses the theory that a "hazardous event" was thought to have occurred at WIV at the time in question, implying that the pandemic could well have started months before the Chinese government said it did. If true, this would almost certainly debunk the natural-origin hypothesis and point to a government coverup. When the story about disappearing cell phone traffic broke, the zoonotic media went through contortions to *explain away* the story in exaggerated, equivocal language. As NBC News reported in May 2020:

> [T]here may have been a "hazardous event" sometime between Oct. 6 and Oct. 11, [but the report] offers no direct evidence of a shutdown, or any proof for the theory that the virus emerged accidentally from the lab. If there was such a shutdown, which has not been confirmed, it could be seen as evidence of a possibility being examined by U.S. intelligence agencies and alluded to by Trump administration officials, including the president—that the novel coronavirus emerged accidentally from the lab.

But that is one of several scenarios under consideration by U.S. intelligence agencies. Many scientists are skeptical, arguing that the more likely explanation is that the virus was transmitted to humans through animals in a Wuhan live produce market. The World Health Organization said Friday it believed the "wet" market played a role in the spread of the disease. (italics added.) [46]

Even in May, NBC was still treating the wet market theory as credible. The fourth NIH condition should not pose a problem because it is old, yet it is condemned along with the rest of the conditions.

Because these conditions implicitly attack the credibility of the zoonotic argument, it is small wonder that Daszak and the pro-zoonotic media threw a collective tantrum at the conditional reinstatement. For example, on Aug. 21, 2020, *Nature* interviewed Daszak for an article that carried the comically febrile headline: "'Heinous!': Coronavirus researcher shut down for Wuhan-lab link slams new funding restrictions." [47] Meanwhile, the zoonotic theory continues to be reflexively defended.

For example, on Nov. 17, 2020, PBS ran a short retrospective piece to coincide with the anniversary of the first case of SARS-CoV-2 in Hubei province. It is not clear what purpose the segment was to serve because the reporter, Patrick Fok, declared its political bias up front:

This is an audiovisual journey that details Chinese Communist Party-led efforts against COVID-19, complete with a timeline of events, according to Chinese authorities, of how they unfolded. [48]

Fok even stood in front of "what's left" of the Huanan market and had the temerity to assert that "many people believe [it] to be the source, the original source of COVID-19."[49] Fok *does* mention criticism of China's lack of openness but not in any way that offered insight. Instead, he used the subject as a springboard to disparage critics of the CCP's version of reality, even to the extent of misrepresenting the lab-origin theory just as the May NBC report did.

> It's . . . helped fuel alternative theories, including the possibility that it might have leaked from the Wuhan Institute of Virology, which had been conducting research on coronaviruses. There's no known evidence to suggest that happened.[50]

The synthetic nature of SARS-CoV-2, the HIV inserts, and the WIV leak represent, respectively, the creation, virulence, and origin of the COVID-19 pandemic. Evidence for these exists, yet it is attacked and dismissed with unscientific hyperbole and cognitive dissonance.

Sources of the Contagion

Chapter 5
Public Health or Biowarfare?

SO FAR IN THIS BOOK, THREE CONCLUSIONS CAN be drawn. First, GoF research is the cause of the mutated genome of SARS-CoV-2. The furin cleavage site and rare arginines (CGGCGG) are enough to prove synthetic origin. Second, GoF research is associated with repeated biosafety failures in China and the U.S., thus proving that the absolute denial of a lab release is untenable. Third, the public-health rationale for GoF research is suspect.

Leaving aside for the moment the perversity of making pathogens more virulent, Daszak's contradictory comments regarding the purpose of the 2014 WIV grant and NIH's conditions for the renewal of the grant point to a less-than-noble motive.

If GoF research can be shown *not* to have a public-health *raison d'être*, then an alternative is a military one, a reasonable inference that has given rise to speculation that SARS-CoV-2 is a bioweapon, an agent of modern germ warfare. Despite official denigration and mockery of the idea, it deserves to be taken seriously.

Dual Use Research of Concern (DURC)

It has long been accepted that tinkering with viruses can have a "dual use" (military) application, but it is always assumed that "enemies" — or to use the current buzzword, "terrorists" — would be the ones to abuse nature for inhuman ends. This is the official U.S. stance on virus manipulation because the *Biological Weapons Anti-Terrorism Act of 1989* (*BWATA*) was passed unanimously by Congress and signed into law by President George H.W. Bush.

Francis Boyle, an expert on germ warfare wrote *BWATA* with the collaboration with the Council for Responsible Genetics, comprised of colleagues from Harvard, Sloan-Kettering and MIT. The impetus, he said, was the Reagan administration's deep investment in genetic engineering for offensive purposes.[1] In fact he considers all GoF research *by definition* to be a violation of the *Act*, and as such wants those responsible for the SARS-CoV-2 pandemic to be held criminally liable under U.S. law:

> [The treaty] provides for life imprisonment for everyone who has done this. I resisted pressure from the Department of Justice with the death penalty in there because I'm opposed to the death penalty for any reason. But all these so-called scientists involved at the University of North Carolina and everyone who funded this project [knew] that it was existentially dangerous and that includes NIAID, Fauci, NIH, and . . . [t]he Dana Harvard Cancer Institute at Harvard . . . One of the variants of criminal intent is the demonstration of grave indifference to human life. And that is the criminal intent necessary for homicide.[2]

Not only does this interpretation of law go a long way toward explaining the desperation of zoonotics to obscure the lab origin of SARS-CoV-2, but it also points to a reason for their rhetorical chicanery. The U.S. ended its offensive biological weapons program in 1969 and signed *BWATA* 20 years later. The U.S. cannot admit that is again developing offensive bioweapons, so it classifies such research as "defensive," but Boyle rejects the euphemism:

> "Biodefense" implies tacit biowarfare, breeding more dangerous pathogens for the alleged purpose of finding a way to fight them. While this work appears to have succeeded in creating deadly and infectious agents, including deadlier flu strains, such "defense" research is impotent in its ability to defend us from this pandemic.[3]

Boyle could well have been referring to a Nov. 9, 2015, paper led by Shi Zhengli and Ralph Baric. In it, the authors state that the University of North Carolina's Institutional Biosafety Committee at Chapel Hill, Baric's university, initiated a study entitled "Generating infectious clones of bat SARS-like CoVs"; Lab Safety Plan ID: 20145741; Schedule G ID: 12279.[4]

Even though this GoF project began before Obama's funding moratorium went into effect, as the authors are at pains to point out, their description of NIH involvement possibly exposed illegal activity: "This paper has been reviewed by the funding agency, the NIH. Continuation of these studies was requested, and this has been approved by the NIH."[5] Under the terms of the moratorium, no new funding was permitted, so it is not clear NIH had the authority to approve a continuation.

As this book has shown, one of the strongest advocates for GoF research is NIH, and in September 2014 it prepared a 77-page "companion guide" for the U.S. government on dual use research. Under the longwinded title *Tools for the Identification, Assessment, Management, and Responsible Communication of Dual Use Research of Concern*, NIH presented a comprehensive treatment of every conceivable aspect of dual use research, such as objectives, oversight mechanisms, risk assessment and management, and institutional review.

The timing of the publication is conspicuous, coming as it does during a period of heightened anxiety over, and criticism of, GoF research. Specifically, it came three months after CDC reported the two accidental releases of pathogens and one month before Obama imposed his new-funding moratorium. One could speculate that NIH got wind of the coming moratorium and wanted to prevent it by casting dual use research in the most responsible light possible. Evidence for this inference comes from an analysis of the language used in the definition of dual use:

> Dual use research is research conducted for legitimate purposes that generates knowledge, information, technologies, and/or products that can be utilized for both benevolent and harmful purposes. Conceivably, much of life sciences research could be considered dual use—that is, most of the information it generates has some potential to be misused. Thus, both DURC policies focus on "dual use research of concern," or "DURC," which is defined as:
>
> Life sciences research that, based on current understanding, can be reasonably anticipated to

provide knowledge, information, products, or technologies that could be directly misapplied to pose a significant threat with broad potential consequences to public health and safety, agricultural crops and other plants, animals, the environment, materiel, or national security.[6]

The neutral way of writing the opening sentence would be, "Dual use research is research conducted to generate knowledge, information, technologies, and/or products that can be utilized for both benevolent and harmful purposes." The question of legitimacy would be assumed, but the need to state "for legitimate purposes" hints that dual use research is *not* legitimate, or is perceived that way. The purpose of the document appears to be to persuade Obama not to halt GoF research funding; however, by drawing attention to the issue of legitimacy, NIH undermined its own argument.

The next sentence is a clumsy piece of rhetorical sleight-of-hand in which the military application of GoF research is obscured by the noble sounding "life sciences research" while "harmful purposes" is softened to "misuse." The third sentence is inane because the authors assume the existence of something not defined (DURC) and then proceed to define it. The overall intent is to complete the moral metamorphosis of dual use research by reinventing it as "dual use research of concern."

The second paragraph externalizes the source of "misapplied" research, and defines DURC as "biodefense." The key feature here is that the threat that DURC is supposed to address is never specified: it is a rhetorical construct, a bogeyman. In short, NIH invented an imaginary threat to justify GoF research and then ennobled it with the euphemism "biodefense," which is virtually interchangeable with "biosecurity."

Biowarfare by any other name

So far, "biosecurity" has appeared twice in this book tangentially in connection with the leak of SARS-CoV-2, but it has been a part of U.S. military planning for decades. The term has been around at least since 2000. At first, it referred to protecting crops and livestock from naturally occurring infectious diseases, such as soybean rust and hoof-and-mouth disease. [7] Since then, the primary purpose of biosecurity has shifted to national security with nature reduced to an afterthought: "to encompass efforts to prevent harm from both intentional and unintentional introductions of organisms to human health and infrastructure and the environment, as well as to the agricultural crop and livestock industry.[8]

However, as Boyle mentioned above, the idea of using biological organisms defensively is a conceptual and moral nonstarter, so GoF research in the service of "biosecurity" must therefore have an offensive purpose despite the absence of an official offensive biological weapons program.

One of the key pieces of evidence of a bioweapon, Boyle said, is that SARS-CoV-2 was created using nanotechnology that aerosolized the virus into microdroplets that can float on the air up to 27 feet:

> That's what you do with nanotechnology. You aerosolize viruses and bacteria to be used as

weapons to be delivered by air in order to be breathed by human beings . . . Fort Detrick does it too. Aerosolization is always the tipoff of a biological warfare weapon. It serves no legitimate scientific or medical purpose at all.[9]

The 1993 Congressional report *Proliferation of Weapons of Mass Destruction: Assessing the Risks* essentially supports Boyle's conclusion. It stated that, like nuclear weapons, a few kilograms of a biological contagion can "kill and disable many thousands of urban residents and seriously impair war-supporting activities."[10] However, because bioweapons take much more time than either nuclear or chemical weapons to have an effect, the ability to mount an effective civilian defense against a biological attack is problematic: "immediate detection and protection are likely to be difficult, and effective advance vaccination may be infeasible."[11]

The connection between the military and bioengineering is also stated overtly in *A National Blueprint for Biodefense,* a militaristic screed put out in October 2015 by the Hudson Institute, about which more later. Its authors assert, among other things, that the biosecurity preparedness of the day lacked focus and coordination, and that the country needed a national strategy based on national, not institutional, funding and centralized political control over biowarfare in the White House, specifically in the Office of the Vice President. Anyone who remembers the "Saddam has WMDs" rumour from 2003 that was invoked to justify the destruction of Iraq will recognize the script. Note the weasel verbs "believe" and "assesses":

Current and former federal officials, as well as a number of private sector experts,[5] *believe* that the biological threat is real and growing, and urge increased activity to defend the nation against it . . . The Department of State *assesses* that China, Iran, North Korea, Russia, and Syria continue to engage in dual-use or biological weapons-specific activities and are failing to comply with the BWC [Biological and Toxin Weapons Convention].[7] Caches of incompletely destroyed or buried biological weapons materials from old state programs[8] can now be accessed again by new state programs, and then smuggled to other regions for use in today's wars and by today's terrorists. (italics added)[12]

The authors go on to praise NIH and NIAID for doing research that is "exceptionally important to defense [sic] against biological terrorism and emerging infectious diseases."[13] Because the linkage between terrorism and infectious diseases is an integral feature, the authors lamented Obama's moratorium for impeding the "critical testing and research" they felt was necessary to counter "the biological threat."[14]

This threat, though, is never proven and has precious little to do with biology or defense. It is selectively invoked to stigmatize nations defined as hostile to corporate America and Israel. In this case the excuse is that these nations are said to be in violation of the *BWC*:

The BWC is a legally binding treaty that entered into force in 1975. Signatory nations agree to never "develop, produce, stockpile or otherwise acquire or retain microbial or other biological agents or toxins whatever their origin or method of production, of types and in quantities that have no justification for prophylactic, protective or other peaceful purposes." To date, 173 nations have become parties to the convention, but at least five of these countries (China, Iran, North Korea, Russia, and Syria) *are suspected of* engaging in biological weapons activities despite BWC ratification. [15] (italics added.)

Not mentioned, of course, is that Israel is not a signatory to the convention and is widely known to have biological as well as chemical and nuclear weapons. [16] Also not mentioned is the U.S.'s self-proclaimed right to violate the convention:

> However, the United States must not allow challenges associated with verification of, compliance with, and enforcement of the BWC to prevent it from exerting leadership in an arena that requires more than diplomatic support of the treaty.[17]

There is a wealth of evidence in this document to support Boyle's contention that "biodefense" is both a rhetorical nonsense and a scientific perversity. Moreover, the fact that an agency like the Hudson Institute published it only supports the view that SARS-CoV-2 is an offensive military instrument.

The institute is a propaganda factory that supports right-wing economic dogma like the abolition of corporate income tax and federally funded Social Security, and warmongering foreign policy. Its Middle East Studies centre is led by the Zionist Meyrav Wurmser, the one-time executive director of the pro-Israel Middle East Media Research Institute (MEMRI). The Hudson Institute is just one a constellation of prowar/anti-democratic "think tanks" that promotes "Isramerican" aggression. [18] Defense in any honest sense is anathema, as can be seen in the names of the co-chairmen of the panel that produced the document: Israel-firster Joe Lieberman, and Thomas Ridge, the first director of DHS.

'An attack on humanity'

Without question the most vigorous and influential exponent of the lab origin/bioweapon theory is Chinese virologist Dr. Yan Liming. Formerly a post-doctorate fellow University of Hong Kong, where she worked in the WHO reference laboratory, she fled China out of fear of reprisals for her dissent from the CCP's official position.

She came to international attention in a Sept. 15 interview with Tucker Carlson on the Fox Network in which she said the bat virus that ostensibly gave rise to SARS-CoV-2 was not harmful to humans until it was modified in a lab owned by China's military.[19] The show aired the day after the publication of a paper in which she and three other researchers presented a detailed refutation of the zoonotic theory.[20] A second paper, published on Oct. 14, lays out Yan's argument that SARS-CoV-2 qualifies as a bioweapon.[21] The two papers are related since the bioweapon argument factors in her alternative theory for the origin of SARS-CoV-2.

To a large extent, Yan and her colleagues' first paper covered familiar ground: debunking the nonsense of the wet-market origin theory and exposing the specious science behind the "discoveries" of RaTG13 and RmYN02. What makes the paper unique, though, is her argument that the genomic backbone for SARS-

CoV-2 likely came from one of two other coronaviruses that were genetically manipulated by China's military:

> The overall genomic/amino acid-level resemblance between SARS-CoV-2 and ZC45/ZXC21 are highly unusual. Such evidence, when considered together, is consistent with a hypothesis that the SARS-CoV-2 genome has an origin based on the use of ZC45/ZXC21 as a backbone and/or template for genetic gain-of-function modifications. Importantly, ZC45 and ZXC21 are bat coronaviruses that were discovered (between July 2015 and February 2017), isolated, and characterized by military research laboratories in the Third Military Medical University (Chongqing, China) and the Research Institute for Medicine of Nanjing Command (Nanjing, China). The data and associated work were published in 2018. Clearly, this backbone/template, which is essential for the creation of SARS-CoV-2, exists in these and other related research laboratories.[22]

The lab origin can be asserted as fact, she wrote, because there is no defensible scenario to explain how ZC45/ZXC21 could acquire a receptor binding domain from another coronavirus to allow it to bind to human ACE2 receptors. This is significant because, she said, ZC45/ZXC21-type coronaviruses *by themselves* cannot infect humans and that SARS-CoV-2 does not bind to bat ACE2 receptors.[23] SARS-CoV-2, therefore, had to be artificially created: "SARS-CoV-2 was well adapted to humans from the start of the outbreak," she wrote.[24] This latter fact also precludes consideration of natural recombination in an intermediate host animal such as pangolins.

Adding to Yan's argument is that the ZC45 and ZXC21 genomes are not contaminated by human engineering, whereas the great store of Shi Zhongli's coronaviruses is suspect because she is known to have engaged in GoF research.[25] Toward the end of the paper, Yan describes the effects of SARS-CoV-2, and ties them to lab origin and military application.

> If it was a laboratory product, the most critical element in its creation, the backbone/template virus (ZC45/ZXC21), is owned by military research laboratories.

> The genome sequence of SARS-CoV-2 has likely undergone genetic engineering, through which the virus has gained the ability to target humans with enhanced virulence and infectivity.

> The characteristics and pathogenic effects of SARS-CoV-2 are unprecedented. The virus is highly transmissible, onset-hidden, multiorgan targeting . . . lethal, and associated with various symptoms and complications.

> SARS-CoV-2 caused a worldwide pandemic, taking hundreds of thousands of lives and shutting down the global economy. It has a destructive power like no other.[26]

In the second paper, Yan and her colleagues again spend much time tearing down RaTG13 and RmYN02 as a buildup to the conclusion that SARS-CoV-2 is a bioweapon. They show how the virus betrays the defining characteristics of a pathogenic bioweapon as determined by Dr. Yang Ruifu, who worked with the UN investigation into Iraq's bioweapons program and is also a leading member of China's National and Military

Bioterrorism Response Consultant Group. In 2005, he wrote that a pathogen had to meet three criteria:

> It is significantly virulent and can cause large scale casualty.
>
> It is highly contagious and transmits easily, often through respiratory routes in the form of aerosols. The most dangerous scenario would be that it allows human-to-human transmission.
>
> It is relatively resistant to environmental changes, can sustain transportation, and is capable of supporting targeted release.[27]

All of these do apply to SARS-CoV-2, but the way the authors use the criteria is more of a political tactic than scientific explanation. The Yan team writes that they included Yang's criteria specifically to address the public perception that SARS-CoV-2 could not be a bioweapon because of its relatively low fatality rate,[28] compared to, for example, SARS-CoV or H5N1 avian flu. Unfortunately, the tactic does not entirely work.

Science or politics—not both

The question of whether SARS-CoV-2 is a bioweapon is really two questions: was it designed that way, and was it deliberately released? Evidence for the former is persuasive, especially Yan's claim that the backbone for SARS-CoV-2 is a military-owned coronavirus that was subjected to genetic manipulation. On the question of deliberate release, though, Yan and her team fall into overstatement. In the "Final discussion and remarks" section, the tone becomes polemical and aggressive as the authors conflate science with their political bias:

> The scientific evidence and records indicate that the current pandemic is not a result of accidental release of a gain-of-function product but a planned attack using an unrestricted bioweapon. The current pandemic therefore should be correspondingly considered as a result of unrestricted biowarfare.[29]

The authors make a good case for the CCP's being responsible for creating SARS-CoV-2, but they cannot prove deliberate release. To assert without empirical or documentary evidence that the CCP committed an "attack on humanity" could damage the scientific value of their work. Even accepting that the feeble cover stories and scientific fabrications were orchestrated by the CCP, it is far easier to argue that these were desperate, clumsy, *ad hoc* measures to cover up an accidental leak caused by incompetence or accident.

The argument that SARS-CoV-2 is a bioweapon is persuasive but not conclusive; however, the matter of CCP responsibility does warrant further investigation.

Chapter 6

Developing Resistance

THIS BOOK HAS SHOWN THAT SARS-COV-2, a man-made, chimeric pathogen, is symptomatic of a much greater threat to humanity: gain-of-function research. Whether or not the research serves the military, the political and financial support lavished on it virtually guarantees that this pandemic will not be the last. In fact, SARS-CoV-2 might not even be the first.

According to Francis Boyle, the 2014-2016 Ebola outbreak in West Africa was the result of U.S. biowarfare vaccine research conducted at BSL4 labs in Liberia, Guinea and Sierra Leone:

> It was a result of testing out of the U.S. biowarfare vaccines at our lab in Kenema, Sierra Leone, that created the West African Ebola pandemic in the first place.[1]

A man-made origin for Ebola is credible because the disease had been unknown in West Africa and gets its name from the Ebola River in northern Democratic Republic of the Congo, some 4,000 kilometers to the southeast of Sierra Leone. In fact, the Ebola outbreak has much in common with SARS-CoV-2: it broke out far from the origin of the virus, came from a lab, and ostensibly began as vaccine research. As for the next pandemic, if it is caused by H5N1 avian flu, there could be 60% fatalities.

The irony is that agencies that profess to be defending people from pandemics, like EcoHealth Alliance and NIH, and respected scientific journals like *Nature* and *Lancet,* are sabotaging efforts to determine the aetiology of SARS-CoV-2 and by extension helping to perpetuate the virus.

One of the most brazen acts of collusion occurred in September 2020 when the newly formed *Lancet* COVID-19 Commission, which was set up to investigate if SARS-CoV-2 might possibly have been the result of a lab leak, named Peter Daszak of all people to lead the investigation. The conflict of interest elicited a chorus of outrage, mockery and disbelief from the scientific community.[2]

Richard Ebright of Rutgers University called Daszak "a misinformation superspreader," and Alina Chan suggested that the commission could have saved time and money by asking WIV to investigate itself.[3]

To appoint someone who has a history of vigorously denigrating a lab leak, concocting sophistries for natural origin and had unethical dealings with the commissioning source, points to yet another coverup, but one so brazen that one wonders why *Lancet* would sully its reputation to no apparent benefit at the expense of public health.

One public interest group, however, *is* trying to get to the bottom of the origin of SARS-CoV-2. U.S Right to Know filed a FOIA request to uncover what role NIH may have played in creating it. Executive Director Gary Ruskin and staff scientist Sainath Suryanarayanan, explained the group's motive in language similar to that of Birger Sørensen and Francis Boyle:

> Preventing the next pandemic may depend crucially on understanding the origins of the present one. We want to know whether the U.S. or Chinese governments, or scientists affiliated with them, are concealing data about the origins of SARS-CoV-2, or the risks of biosafety labs and gain-of-function research.[4]

> We are concerned that data that is crucial to public health policy about the origins of SARS-CoV-2, and the hazards of biosafety laboratories and gain-of-function research, may be hidden within biodefense networks of the national security apparatuses of the United States, China, and elsewhere.[5]

Pharma frenzy

The value of USRTK's work cannot be overemphasized in view of the race to produce a COVID-19 vaccine. Although detailed vaccine analysis is beyond the scope of this book, it is hard to understand how a remedy to a new disease could have been manufactured in less than a year, when an HIV vaccine is still unavailable. By June 5, 2020, 167 vaccine candidates were in pre-clinical development, 13 in phase I or II and 1 in phase II/III.[6]

Specifically, on July 22, 2020—a mere seven to eight months after the start of the pandemic—Pfizer announced a $1.95 billion agreement with HHS and DoD for 100 million doses of the mRNA vaccine BNT162, a type of vaccine that has never been made before. The drug, invented jointly by Pfizer and BioNTech, had received fast-track designation from the U.S. Food and Drug Administration. [7] Other drug companies in the vaccine sweepstakes include Moderna, AstraZeneca and Johnson & Johnson.

An mRNA vaccine causes a person's cells to use mRNA data in the vaccine to create a protein like that of the SARS-CoV-2 spike protein so that the body's immune system will recognise it as an invader and generate antibodies and immune cells.

The unseemly speed with which this untried variety of vaccine is being developed invites questions about such serious matters as what if any corners are being cut, how many false positives or false negatives are being accepted, or what the long-term effects of an mRNA vaccine are. The Trump White House's moniker for vaccine development, "Operation Warp Speed," speaks to a dangerously immature mentality.

Without a proper aetiology of the virus, the conspicuously profitable race for a vaccine brings to mind the biosafety lapses at Chinese and American labs and how haste and inattention to detail might have been responsible for pathogen leaks. The imprimatur of HHS or the DoD, given their involvement in GoF research, is no guarantee of safety, yet the vaccine has been freighted with such hope and deterministic necessity that critical judgment has been all but pre-empted.

In fact, the national-security infrastructure in the U.S. and the U.K. are initiating an Internet offensive using artificial intelligence to attack authors and websites that oppose mass inoculations of the SARS-CoV-2 vaccine.[8] One shopworn tactic will be to stigmatize such sites as coming from Russia or Iran, and the claim will be parroted in the mainstream media.[9]

Because BNT162 or any other COVID-19 vaccine is not the same as a traditional, tested and effective vaccine against diseases like mumps, measles, rubella or diphtheria, resistance based on distrust of testing criteria or efficacy is legitimate. In fact, such resistance could be life-saving. In the journal article "Vaccination against SARS-CoV-2 and disease enhancement—knowns and unknowns," a team of five researchers warned of the possibility of a vaccination causing antibody-dependent enhancement (ADE), which means the antibodies generated by the vaccine could lead to a more severe re-infection:

> The possible risk of vaccine-induced disease enhancement for epidemic coronaviruses has been brought to light during pre-clinical studies with SARS-CoV and MERS-CoV vaccine candidates. It is reasonable to suspect that the same could apply to SARS-CoV-2 since SARS-CoV-2 shares a high degree of sequence homology with SARS-CoV and, to some extent, with MERS-CoV.[10]

Interestingly, ADE does not occur in patients vaccinated against bat coronaviruses.

Is a vaccine even necessary?

Also not adequately analyzed is the reliability of positive COVID-19 reports. Despite the rising death counts, the number of cases of COVID-19 might be drastically overstated such that mass inoculations would be not only needlessly dangerous but unnecessary. The fault lies with the manner of COVID-19 testing.

The procedure used is a Polymerase Chain Reaction (PCR). In the simplest terms, part of the virus's DNA from a blood sample is selected to be copied in a series of cutting (enzyme) and recombination procedures at different temperatures. The reduplications are exponential and is continued until enough of the virus is generated to be detectable. The more cycles the virus sample is put through, the less of the virus there was to begin with, but positive COVID-19 test results do not always include the Cyclic Threshold. This means that not all positive results are the same and not everyone who might test positive is infectious.

Anthony Kuster, a lecturer and researcher in the Faculty of Public Health at Khon Kaen University in Thailand, said if a person has a high viral load, the number of cycles needed to detect the virus will be relatively low, but trace amounts will require a lot more. [11] However, Kuster pointed out that PCR testing is not designed to detect infectiousness, which means it is useless as a diagnostic tool since it cannot distinguish live virus from dead virus.[12]

On Aug. 29, 2020, *The New York Times* reported that a state lab was found to have applied excessive cycles to generate positive results.

> [The lab] analyzed their numbers at the *Times*'s request. In July, the lab identified 872 positive tests, based on a threshold of 40 cycles. With a cut-off of 35, about 43 percent of those tests would no longer qualify as positive. About 63 percent would no longer be judged positive if the cycles were limited to 30.[13]

On the July 16, 2020, online show "This Week in Virology," Fauci even criticized over-cycled PCR tests.:

> "If you get a cycle threshold of 35 or more . . . the chances of it being replication-confident are minuscule . . . You almost never can culture virus from a 37-threshold cycle . . . it's just dead nucleotides, period."[14]

Those who object to mass mRNA vaccination have a right to know how many positive COVID-19 cases have been based on 25, 30 or even 35 cycles.

Even if the vaccine is developed, how useful will it be against mutations? The amino acid sequence 614 on the S1 domain of the SARS-CoV-2 spike protein, for example, shows a change from aspartic acid (D) to glycine (G), which increases infectivity and viral stability and mutates "with an alarming speed"[15]:

> The G614 genotype was not detected in February (among 33 sequences) and observed at low frequency in March (26%), but increased rapidly by April (65%) and May (70%), indicating a transmission advantage over viruses with D614.[16]

The authors of this observation determined that the mutation has a strong affinity for the SARS-CoV-2 furin cleavage site, which might also be what caused the virus to mutate in the first place.[17] Will any vaccine be effective against both strains?

Ultimately, a vaccine is designed merely to treat the symptom of the pandemic, not the cause. GoF research exploited human life in the name of scientific gamesmanship or military irrationality and now the remedy involves more human exploitation on a radically new, insufficiently test kind of vaccine. It is no exaggeration to say that the entire human race has been reduced to guinea pigs. Just like the zoonotic argument, the mass vaccination argument relies on propaganda, censorship and specious science.

In an open letter to the British Health Minister, Michael Yeadon, a former vice-president and chief scientific adviser at Pfizer wrote, in part:

> All vaccines against the SARS-CoV-2 virus are by definition novel. No candidate vaccine has been in development for more than a few months. If any such vaccine is approved for use under any circumstances that are not *explicitly* experimental, I believe that recipients are being misled to a criminal extent.[18]

Index of Names

Index

ENDNOTES

(all Chinese names are written surname last for consistency)

Introduction

1. Greg Felton, *The Host & The Parasite: How Israel's Fifth Colum Consumed America*, 3rd edition (Crestview, FL: Money Tree Publishing, 2018), pp. 267-305. (moneytreepublishing.com/shop/thehosttheparasite).

2. Josh Rogin, "State Department cables warned of safety issues at Wuhan lab studying bat coronaviruses," *The Washington Post*, April 14, 2020, (washingtonpost.com/opinions/2020/04/14/state-department-cables-warned-safety-issues-wuhan-lab-studying-batcoronaviruses).

Science vs. Genetic Fallacy

1. "Pneumonia of unknown cause—China," press release, World Health Organization, Jan. 5, 2020, (who.int/csr/don/05-january-2020-pneumonia-of-unkown-cause-china/en)

2. Cited in "New SARS-like virus can jump directly from bats to humans, no treatment available: Findings provide an opportunity to develop drugs and vaccines for coronaviruses before they emerge from animals to cause a human epidemic." *ScienceDaily,* (sciencedaily.com/releases/2015/11/151110115711.htm).

3. Romeo F. Quijano, M.D., "Origin of COVID-19: Ecological, Historical and Geopolitical Perspective," *Altermedia.net*, April 3, 2020, (altermidya.net/opinion-origin-of-covid-19-ecological-historical-and-geopolitical-perspective).

4. Jon Cohen, "Wuhan seafood market may not be source of novel virus spreading globally," *Science*, Jan. 26, 2020, (sciencemag.org/news/2020/01/wuhan-seafood-market-may-not-be-source-novel-virus-spreading-globally). For a detailed analysis that rules out the market see Shing Hei Zhan, Benjamin E. Deverman and Yujia Alina Chan, *SARS-CoV-2 is well adapted*

Endnotes

for humans. What does this mean for re-emergence? BioRxiv, May 2, 2020, (doi.org/10.1101/2020.05.01.073262).

5. Peng Zhou, et al., "A pneumonia outbreak associated with a new coronavirus of probable bat origin," Nature, No. 579, Feb. 3, 2020, (doi.org/10.1038/s4158602020127).

6. Ibid.

7. Ibid.

8. Rebecca Weisser, "China's Frankenstein virus—Does this monster have French and American uncles?" *Spectator Australia,* May 30, 2020, (spectator.com.au/2020/05/chinas-frankenstein-virus).

9. "Shu Kang" "RaTG13–the undeniable evidence that the Wuhan coronavirus is man-made," May 28, 2020, (*nerdhaspower.weebly. com/ratg13isfake.html*). See also (youtube.com/watch?v=jnQKu2h VYVQ). "Shu Kang" is a pseudonym assumed for personal safety reasons.

10. Manthan Chheda, "Coronavirus samples derived from bats stored in Wuhan lab for 7 years?" *International Business Times,* April 10, 2020.

11. Xingyi Ge, et al, "Coexistence of multiple coronaviruses in several bat colonies in an abandoned mineshaft," *Virologica Sinica,* February 2016, Vol. 31 Issue 1, (doi.org/10.1007/s1225001637139).

12. M.C Rahalkar and R.A Bahulikar, "Understanding the Origin of 'BatCoVRaTG13', a Virus Closest to SARS-CoV-2," *Preprints* 2020, 2020050322 (doi: 10.20944/preprints202005.0322.v1)

13. *Virologica Sinica,* February 2016, note 11.

14. *Nature,* Feb. 3, 2020, note 5.

15. Jon Cohen, "Wuhan coronavirus hunter Shi Zhengli speaks out," *Science,* July 31, 2020, (science.sciencemag.org/content/369/6503/487.full).

16. Yuri Deigin, "LabMade? SARS-CoV-2 Genealogy Through the Lens of Gain-of-Function Research," *medium.com,* April 22, 2020, (yurideigin.medium.com/lab-made-cov2-genealogy-through-the-lens-of-gain-of-function-research-f96dd7413748).

17. *Virologica Sinica,* February 2016, note 11.

18. George Arbuthnot et al., "Revealed: Seven-year coronavirus-trail from mine deaths to a Wuhan lab," *Sunday Times,* July 4,

2020, (thetimes.co.uk/article/seven-year-covid-trail-revealed l5vxt7jqp), archived at (archive.fo/LPCD1).

19. Cited in Jennifer Kahn, "How Scientists Could Stop the Next Pandemic Before It Starts," *New York Times Magazine*, April 21, 2020, (nytimes.com/2020/04/21/magazine/pandemicvaccine.html).

20. Alina Chan, @AyChan, July 8, 2020, (twitter.com/Ayjchan/status/1279761424919732224).

21. Steven W. Mosher, "Was the coronavirus created by Chinese scientist who tried to cover her tracks—and failed?" *LifeSite News*, May 15, 2020, (lifesitenews.com/blogs/was-the-coronavirus-created-by-chinese-scientist-who-tried-to-cover-her-tracks-and-failed).

22. Xiaoxu Lin and Shizhong Chen, "Major Concerns on the Identification of Bat Coronavirus Strain RaTG13 and Quality of Related *Nature* Paper," *Preprints* 2020, 2020060044, (doi: 10.20944/preprints202006.0044.v1).

23. *Sunday Times*, July 4, 2020.

24. Charles Calisher, et al., "Statement in support of the scientists, public health professionals, and medical professionals of China combatting COVID-19," *The Lancet*, Vol. 395, March 7, 2020, (thelancet.com/journals/lancet/article/PIIS01406736(20)304189/fulltext).

25. Kristian Andersen, et al., "The proximal origin of SARS-CoV-2," *virological.org*, Feb. 16, 2020, (virological.org/t/the-proximal-origin-of-SARS-CoV-2/398). For a discussion of Andersen and his rubbishing of the synthetic origin of SARS-CoV-2, see Chapter 3.

26. "EcoHealth Alliance orchestrated key scientists' statement on "natural origin of SARS-CoV-2—Biohazard_FOIA_Maryland_Emails_11.6.20.pdf" *U.S. Right to Know*, p. 251 (first reference), (usrtk.org/wpcontent/uploads/2020/11/Biohazard_FOIA_Maryland_Emails_11.6.20.pdf).

27. Ibid., p. 266.

28. Ibid. p. 263.

29. Alina Chan, "Timeline of SARS-CoV-2related virus data published in late 20192020," (twitter.com/Ayjchan/status/1320345474646290434).

30. Ibid.

31. Ibid, twitter.com/Ayjchan/status/1320356596392906752.

Endnotes

32. Ibid, twitter.com/Ayjchan/status/1320359968692895750 photo/1).

33. D. Kanduc and Y. Shoenfeld, "Molecular mimicry between SARS-CoV-2 spike glycoprotein and mammalian proteomes: implications for the vaccine." *Immunological Research* vol. 68, Sept. 18, 2020, pp. 310–313, (doi.org/10.1007/s12026020091526).

34. Whereas a genome merely depicts the genetic makeup of an organism, a proteome is *dynamic* in that it shows the genome interacting with external factors such as "the state of development, tissue type, metabolic state, and various interactions." M. De Angelis, M. Calasso, Molecular Biology: BIOLOGY | Proteomics, Editor(s): Carl A. Batt, Mary Lou Tortorello, *Encyclopedia of Food Microbiology* (Second Edition), Academic Press, 2014, pp. 793-802, (sciencedirect.com/science-article/pii/B978012384730000003761).

35. Kanduc and Shoenfeld, 2020, pp. 311-312.

36. *WHO-convened Global Study of the Origins of SARS-CoV-2: Terms of References for the China Part, World Health Organization,* July 31, 2020, pp. 2-5 (who.int/publications/m/item/who-convened-global-study-of-the-origins-of-sars-cov-2).

37. Kirti Pandey, "WHO team on mission to trace origin of COVID-19 in China returns without visit to Wuhan, stirs controversy," *timesnownews.com*, Aug. 28, 2020, (timesnownews.com/international/article/who-team-on-mission-to-trace-origin-of-covid-19-in-china-returns-without-visit-to-wuhan-stirs-controversy/644202).

38. Ibid.

39. Selam Gebrekidan, Matt Apuzzo, Amy Qin and Javier C. Hernández, "In Hunt for Virus Source, WHO Let China Take Charge," *New York Times*, Nov. 2, 2020, (nytimes.com/2020/11/02/world/who-china-coronavirus.html).

40. Ibid.

41. "COVID-19 Coronavirus Pandemic," *worldometers.info*, (worldometers.info/coronavirus).

SARS-CoV vs. SARS-CoV-2

1. "SARS (10 Years After)," Centers for Disease Control and Prevention, last reviewed March 3, 2016, (cdc.gov/dotw/sars/index.html).

2. "Coronavirus deaths exceed Sars fatalities in 2003," BBC, Feb. 9, 2020, (bbc.com/news/worldasiachina51431087).

3. For an example, see Chapter 1, note 1.

4. Annalise E. Zemlin, and Owen J. Wiese. "Coronavirus disease 2019 (COVID-19) and the renin-angiotensin system: A closer look at angiotensin-converting enzyme 2 (ACE2)." *Annals of clinical biochemistry* vol. 57,5 (2020): 339350. (doi:10.1177/0004563220928361).

5. Krishna Sriram, et al., "What is the ACE2 receptor, how is it connected to coronavirus and why might it be key to treating COVID-19? The experts explain," *The Conversation*, May 14, 2020, (theconversation.com/what-is-the-ace2-receptor-how-is-it-connected-to-coronavirus-and-why-might-it-be-key-to-treating-covid-19-the-experts-explain-136928).

6. Liji Thomas MD, "A closer look at TMPRSS2: This could help treat COVID-19," newsmedical.net, May 28, 2020, (news-medical.net/news/20200528/A-closer-look-at-TMPRSS2-This-could-help-treat-COVID-19.aspx).

7. "Novel coronavirus structure reveals targets for vaccines and treatments," National Institutes of Health, March 3, 2020, (nih.gov/news-events/nih-research-matters/novel-coronavirus-structure-reveals-targets-vaccines-treatments).

8. Rebecca Weisser, "China's Frankenstein virus — Does this monster have French and American uncles?" *Spectator Australia*, May 30, 2020, (spectator.com.au/2020/05/chinas-frankenstein-virus).

9. Berend Jan Bosch, et al. "Cathepsin L Functionally Cleaves the Severe Acute Respiratory Syndrome Coronavirus Class I Fusion Protein Upstream of Rather than Adjacent to the Fusion Peptide," *Journal of Virology*, August 2008, Vol. 82, No. 17, pp. 8887-8890; (doi: 10.1128/JVI.0041508.).

10. Javier A. James, et al., "Proteolytic Cleavage of the SARS-CoV-2 Spike Protein and the Role of the Novel S1/S2 Site," *iScience*, vol. 23, pp. 101-212, June 26, 2020, (cell.com/iscience/fulltext/S25890042(20)303977).

11. Kathryn E. Follis, et al. "Furin cleavage of the SARS coronavirus spike glycoprotein enhances cell-cell fusion but does not affect virion entry." *Virology* vol. 350, 2 (2006), pp. 358-369. (doi:10.1016/j.virol.2006.02.003).

12. Ibid.

13. Aiping Wu, et al., "Genome Composition and Divergence of the Novel Coronavirus (2019nCoV) Originating in China," *Cell Host & Microbe*, March 11, 2020, (doi.org/10.1016/j.chom.2020.02.001).

14. Rossana Segreto, "Is considering a genetic-manipulation origin for SARS-CoV-2 a conspiracy theory that must be censored," *Research Gate*, April 2020, (researchgate.net/publication/340924249_ Is_ considering_a_geneticmanipulation_origin_for_SARS-CoV-2_a_conspiracy_theory_that_must_be_censored).

15. Steven W. Mosher, "Was the coronavirus created by Chinese scientist who tried to cover her tracks—and failed?" *LifeSite News*, May 15, 2020, (lifesitenews.com/blogs/was-the-coronavirus-created-by-chinese-scientist-who-tried-to-cover-her-tracks-and-failed).

16. "A close relative of SARS-CoV-2 found in bats offers more evidence it evolved naturally," *Cell Press*, May 11, 2020, (phys.org/news/2020-05-relative-sars-cov-evidence-evolved-naturally.html). See also, Jacinta Bowler, "Researchers Find Another Virus in Bats That's Closely Related to SARS-CoV-2," *Science Alert*, May 12, 2020, (sciencealert.com/researchers-have-found-another-close-relative-of-sars-cov-2-in-bats).

17. Hong Zhou, et al, "A Novel Bat Coronavirus Closely Related to SARS-CoV-2 Contains Natural Insertions at the S1/S2 Cleavage Site of the Spike Protein," *Current Biology*, vol. 30 issue 11, May 10, 2020, (doi.org/10.1016/j.cub.2020.05.023).

18. *Cell Press*, 2020, note 16.

19. Ibid.

Chimeric Virus

1. Cited in Talha Burki, "Ban on gain-of-function studies ends." *The Lancet. Infectious diseases* vol. 18, 2 (2018): 148149. (doi: 10.1016/S14733099(18)300069).

2. Ibid. For the statement by the Cambridge Working Group opposing GoF research and a list of its founding signatories and members see Group and its signatories see (cambridgeworking group.org).

3. Milton Leitenberg, "Did the SARS-CoV-2 virus arise from a bat coronavirus research program in a Chinese laboratory? Very possibly." *Bulletin of the Atomic Scientists*, June 4, 2020, (thebulletin.org/2020/06/

did-the-sars-cov-2-virus-arise-from-a-bat-coronavirus-research-program-in-a-chinese-laboratory-very-possibly).

4. Gonzalo Izaguirre, "The Proteolytic Regulation of Virus Cell Entry by Furin and Other Proprotein Convertases." *Viruses* vol. 11, no.9, Sept. 9, 2019, (doi:10.3390/v11090837). See also Markus Hoffman et al., "A Multibasic Cleavage Site in the Spike Protein of SARS-CoV-2 Is Essential for Infection of Human Lung Cells," *Molecular Cell*, Volume 78, Issue 4, P779784.e5, May 21, 2020 (doi.org/10.1016/j.molcel.2020.04.022).

5. Yu Li et al., "The MERS-CoV Receptor DPP4 as a Candidate Binding Target of the SARS-CoV-2 Spike," *iScience,* Volume 23, Issue 6, 101160, June 26, 2020, (doi.org/10.1016/j.isci.2020.1011600.

6. Stephen Chen, "Coronavirus far more likely than SARS to bond to human cells due to HIV-like mutation, scientists say," *South China Morning Post*, Feb. 27, 2020, (scmp.com/news/ china/society/ article/3052495/coronavirus-far-more-likely-sars-bond-human-cells-scientists-say). The date on this information is significant because it predates by about one month the Chinese government's censorship of academic opinion. See Chapter 4, note 4.

7. Ibid.

8. Birgen Sørensen et al., "Biovacc19: A Candidate Vaccine for COVID-19 (SARS-CoV-2) Developed from Analysis of its General Method of Action for Infectivity," *QRB Discovery*, 117, June 2, 2020, (doi:10.1017/qrd.2020.8). CD4 (Cluster of Differentiation 4) is a white blood cell (Tcell) that fights infection.

9. For a discussion of antibody-dependent enhancement (ADE), see Chapter 6.

10. Sørensen et al., 2020.

11. "Norwegian scientist Birger Sorensen claims coronavirus was lab-made and 'not natural in origin'," *techstartups.com*, June 7, 2020, (techstartups.com/2020/06/07/Norwegian-scientist-birger-sorensen-claims-coronavirus-lab-made-not-natural-origin).

12. Dan Samorodnitsky, "Don't believe the conspiracy theories you hear about coronavirus and HIV," massivesci.com, Jan. 31, 2020, (https://massivesci.com/notes/wuhan-coronavirus-ncov-sars-mers-hiv-human-immunodeficiency-virus). Note that this rant comes out at the end of January.

Endnotes

13. Joseph Mercola, "Forbes Caught in Blatant Censoring Act," *Lewrockwell.com*, June 25, 2020, (lewrockwell.com/2020/06/joseph-mercola/forbes-caught-in-blatant-censoring-act). Lew Rockwell has also archived the original article.

14. Ibid.

15. See Table III for the names of the amino acids.

16. In all, three researchers were interviewed about the paper in a series of interviews conducted between Sept. 1 and 25, 2020. However, because of unwanted publicity over misrepresentations of their findings, they have asked not to be identified.

17. Interview with the author, 7:30-8:30 PDT, Sept. 8, 2020.

18. Ibid. One site where the paper can still be found is greatgameindia.com/uncanny-similarity-of-unique-inserts-in-the-2019-ncov-spike-protein-to-hiv1-gp120-and-gag.

19. Jon Cohen, "Trump 'owes us an apology.' Chinese scientist at the center of COVID-19 origin theories speaks out," *Science*, July, 24, 2020, (sciencemag.org/news/2020/07/trump-owes-us-apology-chinese-scientist-center-covid-19-origin-theories-speaks-out).

Sources of the Contagion

1. Henry Holloway," Controversial Wuhan lab admits it had THREE live coronavirus strains before pandemic – but insists none match COVID-19," *The Sun*, May 26, 2020, (thesun.co.uk/news/11710670/wuhan-lab-admits-coronavirus-china-covid-19).

2. "How virus research has become a point of tension for the U.S. and China," *PBS News Hour*, May 26, 2020, (pbs.org/newshour/show/how-virus-research-has-become-a-point-of-tension-for-the-u-s-and-china).

3. "General Secretary Xi Jinping Chairs 12th Meeting of Central Commission for Comprehensively Deepening Reform," Ministry of Foreign Affairs, Feb. 14, 2020, (fmprc.gov.cn/mfa_eng/zxxx_662805/t1745270.shtml).

4. Elena Pavlovska, "China censors coronavirus research, bars publication of key findings," *New Europe*, April 13, 2020, (neweurope.eu/article/china-censors-coronavirus-research-bars-publication-of-key-findings).

5. Josh Rogin, "State Department cables warned of safety issues at Wuhan lab studying bat coronaviruses," *The Washington Post*, April 14, 2020, (washingtonpost.com/opinions/2020/04/14/state-department-cables-warned-safety-issues-wuhan-lab-studying-bat-coronaviruses).

6. Matt Field, "Experts know the new coronavirus is not a bioweapon. They disagree on whether it could have leaked from a research lab," *Bulletin of the Atomic Scientists*, March 30, 2020, (thebulletin.org/2020/03/experts-know-the-new-coronavirus-is-not-a-bioweapon-they-disagree-on-whether-it-could-have-leaked-from-a-research-lab).

7. See Chapter 1, note 1.

8. Greg Felton, "Chapter 11," *The Host & The Parasite: How Israel's Fifth Column Consumed America*," 3rd ed., (Crestview, FL: Money Tree Publishing, 2018).

9. Robert Walgate, "SARS escaped Beijing lab twice," *Genome Biology*, April 27, 2004, (doi.org/10.1186/gbspotlight2004042703).

10. Ibid.

11. *PBS News Hour*, May 26, 2020.

12. Philippe Reltien, "*Enquête sur le P4 de Wuhan, ce laboratoire qui suscite tant de fantasmes, construit avec l'aide de la France*," Radio France, April 17, 2020, (franceinter.fr/monde/enquete-sur-le-p4-de-wuhan-ce-laboratoire-qui-suscite-tant-de-fantasmes-construit-avec-laide-de-la-france). Unless otherwise indicated, this account of the origin of the origin of the P4 (BSL4) Wuhan lab section is based on a relevant summary of the April 17, 2020, Radio France investigative report. Translation from the French by the author.

13. Declan Butler, "Engineered bat virus stirs debate over risky research," *Nature*, Nov. 12, 2015, (nature.com/news/engineered bat-virus-stirs-debate-over-risky-research-1.18787).

14. Ibid.

15. "Coronavirus and China: unconfirmed origin in Wuhan laboratory, but unconvincing denial," *fr24news.com*, April 3, 2020, (fr24news.com/a/2020/04/coronavirus-and-china-unconfirmed-origin-in-wuhan-laboratory-but-unconvincing-denial.html).

16. Field, 2020. Huang's source is a report from the South China University of Technology.

17. *The Washington Post*, April 14, 2020.

18. "CDC Director Releases AfterAction Report on Recent Anthrax Incident; Highlights Steps to Improve Laboratory Quality and Safety," CDC press release, July 11, 2014, (cdc.gov/media/releases/2014/p0711labsafety.html).

19. Ibid.

20. "Accidental Exposure in Biosafety Laboratories, various sources, (stopthebiolab.files.wordpress.com/2011/07/accidentslist.pdf). The intentional release occurred in November 2001 when letters laced with anthrax were mailed to Democratic senators Patrick Leahy and Tom Daschle. Five people died and 17 others were infected. It was reported that these letters were another act of "terrorism" according to the official narrative of the WTC/Pentagon attack, but the source of the pathogen was later traced to the U.S. Army Medical Research Institute of Infectious Diseases at Ft. Detrick, MD. The researcher responsible was declared to be Bruce E. Ivins, an Army biodefense expert, but evidence is inconclusive. He committed suicide in 2008, according to the FBI. The fact that this attack was a case of domestic violence fits with the self-inflicted nature of the Sept. 11, 2001, attacks.

21. "Doing Diligence to Assess the Risks and Benefits of Life Sciences Gain-of-function Research," White House press release, Oct. 17, 2014, (obamawhitehouse.archives.gov/blog/2014/10/17/doing-diligence-assess-risks-and-benefits-life-sciences-gain-function-research).

22. Christina Lin, "Why US outsourced bat virus research to Wuhan," *Asia Times*, April 20, 2020, (asiatimes.com/2020/04/why-us-outsourced-bat-virus-research-to-wuhan).

23. Alexis Bayden-Mayer, "Peter 'Show Me the Money' Daszak Pulls in Big Bucks, through EcoHealth Alliance, for Risky Virus 'Research'," *Organic Consumers Association*, Sept. 3, 2020, (organicconsumers.org/blog/peter-show-me-money-daszak-pulls-big-bucks-through-ecohealth-alliance-risky-virus-research).

24. Meredith Wadman, Jon Cohen, "NIH's axing of bat coronavirus grant a 'horrible precedent' and might break rules, critics say," *Science*, April 30, 2020, (sciencemag.org/news/2020/04/nih-s-axing-bat-coronavirus-grant-horrible-precedent-and-might-break-rules-critics-say). In 2008, long before WIV was built, NIAID gave EcoHealth a four-year, $2.6-million grant to study the risk for viral emergence from bats.

25. Ibid.

26. "Notice Announcing the Removal of the Funding Pause for Gain-of-function Research Projects," National Institutes of Health, Dec. 19, 2017, (grants.nih.gov/grants/guide/noticefiles/NOTOD 17071.html).

27. Ibid. For a list of corporate, governmental, academic and other partners, see *ecohealthalliance.org/partners.*

28. Lisa Schnirring, "Feds lift gain-of-function research pause, offer guidance," *CIDRAP News,* Dec. 19, 2017, (cidrap.umn.edu/newsperspective/2017/12/feds-lift-gain-function-research-pause-offer-guidance).

29. Jocelyn Kaiser, "EXCLUSIVE: Controversial experiments that could make bird flu more risky poised to resume," *Science,* Feb. 8, 2019, (sciencemag.org/news/2019/02/exclusive-controversial-experiments-make-bird-flu-more-risky-poised-resume). The first results of GoF funding approvals were leaked to *Science,* which was the first to alert the public to the renewed funding of GoF experiments. (organicconsumers.org/blog/covid-19-reckless-gain-of-function-experiments-lie-at-the-root-of-the-pandemic).

30. Chip Somodevilla, "Dr. Fauci Backed Controversial Wuhan Lab with U.S. Dollars for Risky Coronavirus Research," *Newsweek,* April 28, 2020, (newsweek.com/dr-fauci-backed-controversial-wuhan-lab-millions-us-dollars-risky-coronavirus-research-1500741).

31. Ibid.

32. Peter Daszak, "Understanding the Risk of Bat Coronavirus Emergence," *Project Reporter*, July 24, 2019.

33. "Dr Fauci Funded Wuhan Virus Experiments — Former NY Mayor," *Great Game India Journal on Geopolitics and International Relations*, April 27, 2020, (greatgameindia.com/dr-fauci-funded-wuhan-virus-experiments-former-ny-mayor). The radio show is in an embedded audio link.

34. "Partial transcript of email exchanges in which NIH cuts off grant funding to EcoHealth Alliance," *Science*, April 30, 2020, (sciencemag.org/sites/default/files/Lauer.Daszak.NIH grant killed.partial email transcripts.April 2020.pdf).

35. David Lim and Brianna Ehley, "Fauci says White House told NIH to cancel funding for bat virus study," *politico.com*, June 23,

2020, (politico.com/news/2020/06/23/fauci-nih-white-house-bat-study-336452).

36. Meredith Wadman and Jon Cohen, "NIH's axing of bat coronavirus grant a 'horrible precedent' and might break rules, critics say," *Science*, April 30, 2020, (sciencemag.org/news/2020/04/nih-s-axing-bat-coronavirus-grant-horrible-precedent-and-might-break-rules-critics-say).

37. James Gorman, "Prominent Scientists Denounce End to Coronavirus Grant," *The New York Times*, May 21, 2020, (nytimes.com/2020/05/21/health/wuhan-coronavirus-laboratory.html).

38. Lim and Ehley, June 23, 2020.

39. See note 28.

40. Jie Cui et al. "Origin and evolution of pathogenic coronaviruses," *Nature*, Dec. 10, 2018, (nature.com/articles/s4157901801189).

41. See note 30.

42. Cited in Betsy McKay, "NIH Presses U.S. Nonprofit for Information on Wuhan Virology Lab," *Wall Street Journal*, Aug. 19, 2020, (wsj.com/articles/nih-presses-us-non-profit-for-information-on-wuhan-virology-lab-11597829400).

43. The link here takes the reader to the preprint paper that mentions RaTG13 for the first time, 12 day before the infamous *Nature* paper. Peng Zhou, et al. "Discovery of a novel coronavirus associated with the recent pneumonia outbreak in humans and its potential bat origin," *Biorxiv.org*, Jan. 22, 2020, (biorxiv.org/content/10.1101/2020.01.22.914952v2.full.pdf).

44. Meredith Wadman, "NIH Imposes 'Outrageous' Conditions on Resuming Coronavirus Grant Targeted by Trump," *Pulitzer Center*, Aug. 20, 2020, (pulitzercenter.org/reporting/nih-imposes-outrageous-conditions-resuming-coronavirus-grant-targeted-trump).

45. *Newsweek*, April 28, 2020, note 30.

46. Ken Dilanian, et al. "Report says cellphone data suggests October shutdown at Wuhan lab, but experts are skeptical," *NBCNews.com*, May 8, 2020, (nbcnews.com/politics/national-security/report-says-cellphone-data-suggests-october-shutdown-wuhan-lab-experts-n1202716).

47. Nidhi Subbaraman, "'Heinous!': Coronavirus researcher shut down for Wuhan-lab link slams new funding restrictions," *Nature*, Aug. 21, 2020, (nature.com/articles/d41586020024734).

48. Patrick Fok, "A year after virus appeared, Wuhan tells China's pandemic story," *PBS News Hour*, Nov. 17, 2020, (pbs.org/newshour/show/a-year-after-virus-appeared-wuhan-tells-chinas-pandemic-story).

49. Ibid.

50. Ibid.

Public Health or Biowarfare?

1. Dr. Francis Boyle, *Basically, humanity is fighting World War III against COVID-19*, paper presented at the International Conference on Eradication of Biological and Chemical Weapons, Maharashtra Institute of Technology World Peace University (Pune), India, June 2326, 2020, (thehansindia.com/my-voice/basically-humanity-is-fighting-world-war-iii-against-covid-19-649426).

2. Dr. Francis Boyle, interview with Dr. Joseph Mercola, *SARS-CoV-2: A Possible Form of Biological Warfare*, March 8, 2020, (organicconsumers.org/sites/default/files/interview-francisboyle-sars-cov-2.pdf).

3. Ibid.

4. Vineet D. Menachery, et al. "A SARS-like cluster of circulating bat coronaviruses shows potential for human emergence." *Nature medicine* vol. 21,12 (2015): 150813, (doi:10.1038/nm.3985).

5. Ibid.

6. "Tools for the Identification, Assessment, Management, and Responsible Communication of Dual Use Research of Concern: A Companion Guide to the United States Government Policies for Oversight of Life Sciences Dual Use Research of Concern," NIH, September 2014, p. 7, (phe.gov/s3/dual-use/Documents/durc-companion-guide.pdf).

7. Laura A. Meyerson, Jamie K. Reaser, "Biosecurity: Moving toward a Comprehensive Approach: A comprehensive approach to biosecurity is necessary to minimize the risk of harm caused by nonnative organisms to agriculture, the economy, the environment, and human health," *BioScience*, Volume 52, Issue 7,

Endnotes

July 2002, pp. 593–600, (doi.org/10.1641/00063568(2002)052 [0593:BMTACA]2.0.CO;2).

8. Ibid.

9. Boyle, June 23-26, 2020.

10. *Proliferation of Weapons of Mass Destruction: Assessing the Risks, OTA-ISC-559,* , (Washington, D.C.: U.S. Congress, Office of Technology Assessment, August 1993), p. 62.

11. Ibid.

12. Joseph I. Lieberman et al., *A National Blueprint for Defense,* Hudson Institute, October 2015, p. 4, (biodefensecommission.org/reports/a-national-blueprint-for-biodefense).

13. Ibid. p. 7

14. Ibid, p. 48.

15. Ibid.

16. U.S. Congress 1993, pp. 64-68.

17. Liberman, et al. 2015, p. 48.

18. Greg Felton, "Chapter 5," *The Host & The Parasite: How Israel's Fifth Column Consumed America,"* 3rd ed., (Crestview, FL: Money Tree Publishing, 2018).

19. "Coronavirus whistleblower speaks out about possible COVID origin on 'Tucker'," FoxNews, Sept. 15, 2020 (youtube.com/watch?v=qFlqXPl_hZQ).

20. LiMeng Yan, et al., *Unusual Features of the SARS-CoV-2 Genome Suggesting Sophisticated Laboratory Modification Rather Than Natural Evolution and Delineation of Its Probable Synthetic Route,* (New York: Rule of Law Society and Rule of Law Foundation, Sept. 14, 2020, zenodo.org/record/4028830).

21. LiMeng Yan, et al., *SARS-CoV-2 Is an Unrestricted Bioweapon: A Truth Revealed through Uncovering a LargeScale, Organized Scientific Fraud,* (New York: Rule of Law Society and Rule of Law Foundation, Sept. 14, 2020, zenodo.org/record/4073131).

22. Yan et al., Sept. 14, 2020, p. 5.

23. Ibid, pp. 89.

24. Ibid p. 9.

25. Ibid. p. 16.

26. Ibid. p. 21.

27. Yanet al., Oct. 14, 2020, p. 26.

28. Ibid.

29. Ibid, p. 27.

Developing Resistance

1. Dr. Francis Boyle interview with Sherwood Ross, "Boyle Charges U.S. Germ Warfare Program is 'Criminal Enterprise'," March 8, 2020, (worldbeyondwar.org/boyle-charges-us-germ-warfare-program-is-criminal-enterprise).

2. Jonathan Matthews, "Scientists outraged by Peter Daszak leading enquiry into possible Covid lab leak," *gmwatch*, Sept. 23, 2020, (gmwatch.org/en/news/latest-news/19538-scientists-outraged-by-peter-daszak-leading-enquiry-into-possible-covid-lab-leak).

3. Ibid.

4. "U.S. Right to Know Sues NIH for Documents about Origins of SARS-CoV-2," *usrtk.org*, Nov. 5, 2020, (usrtk.org/news-releases/u-s-right-to-know-sues-nih-for-documents-about-origins-of-sars-cov-2)

5. Sainath Suryanarayanan, "Why we are researching the origins of SARS-CoV-2, biosafety labs and GOF research," *usrtk.org*, Oct. 13, 2020, (usrtk.org/biohazards/why-we-are-researching-the-origins-of-sars-cov-2-biosafety-labs-and-gof-research).

6. Raphaël M. Zellweger, et al. "Vaccination against SARS-CoV-2 and disease enhancement—knowns and unknowns," *Expert Review of Vaccines*, vol. 8, no. 8, Aug. 24, 2020, p. 691) doi: 10.1080/14760584.2020.1800463).

7. "Pfizer and BioNTech Announce an Agreement with U.S. Government for up to 600 Million Doses of mRNAbased Vaccine Candidate Against SARS-CoV-2," *pfizer.com*, July 22, 2020, (pfizer.com/news/press-release/press-release-detail/pfizer-and-biontech-announce-agreement-us-government-600).

8. Whitney Webb, "Cyber War Declared in U.S. and UK to Quash Vaccine Hesitancy as Nations Prepare for Mass Inoculations," *The Defender*, Nov. 16, 2020, (childrenshealthdefense.org/defender/cyber-war-declared-u-s-u-k-vaccine-hesitancy-prepare-mass-inoculations).

Endnotes

9. Ibid.

10. Zellweger, 2020, p. 692.

11. Anthony Kuster, *COVID Diagnosis with PCR | Misinterpreting results | Cycle threshold explained,* YouTube, Sept. 19, 2020, (youtube.com/watch?v=S_1Z8cSXI-Q).

12. Ibid.

13. Apoorva Mandavilli, "Your Coronavirus Test Is Positive. Maybe It Shouldn't Be." *The New York Times,* Sept. 17, 2020, (nytimes.com/2020/08/29/health/coronavirus-testing.html).

14. "This Week in Virology," *microbe.tv,* (youtube.com/watch?v=a_Vy6fgaBPE).

15. Lizhou Zhang, Cody B. Jackson, et al. "The D614G mutation in the SARS-CoV-2 spike protein reduces S1 shedding and increases infectivity," *researchgate.net,* June, 2020, p. 3. (doi: 10.1101/2020.06.12.148726).

16. Ibid.

17. Ibid p. 9.

18. Cited in Joseph Mercola, "Former Pfizer Science Officer Reveals Great COVID-19 Scam," *mercola.com,* Nov. 25, 2020, (articles.mercola.com/sites/articles/archive/2020/11/25/michael-yeadon-pfizer-coronavirus-scam.aspx).